INSTRUCTOR AND ADJUNCT SUPPORT MANUAL

INTERMEDIATE ALGEBRA: GRAPHS & MODELS

THIRD EDITION

Marvin L. Bittinger
Indiana University Purdue University Indianapolis

David J. Ellenbogen
Community College of Vermont

Barbara L. Johnson
Indiana University Purdue University Indianapolis

PEARSON

Addison
Wesley

Boston San Francisco New York
London Toronto Sydney Tokyo Singapore Madrid
Mexico City Munich Paris Cape Town Hong Kong Montreal

Reproduced by Pearson Addison-Wesley from electronic files supplied by the authors.

Copyright © 2008 Pearson Education, Inc.
Publishing as Pearson Addison-Wesley, 75 Arlington Street, Boston, MA 02116.

ISBN-13: 978-0-321-42856-1
ISBN-10: 0-321-42856-0

1 2 3 4 5 6 OPM 10 09 08 07

CONTENTS

INTRODUCTION

Dear Faculty:

The Bittinger/Ellenbogen/Johnson book team at Pearson Addison-Wesley is very excited that you will be using *Intermediate Algebra: Graphs and Models*, Third Edition. We know that whether you are teaching this course for the first time or the tenth time, you will face many challenges, including how to prepare for class, how to make the most effective use of your class time, how to present the material to your students in a manner that will make sense to them, how best to assess your students, and the list goes on.

This manual is designed to make your job easier. Inside these pages are words of advice from experienced instructors, general and content-specific teaching tips, a list of the objectives covered within *Intermediate Algebra: Graphs and Models*, descriptions of both student and instructor supplements that accompany this text, and a list of valuable resources provided by your fellow instructors.

We would like to thank the following professors for sharing their advice and teaching tips. This manual would not be what it is without their valuable contribution.

Kandace Kling, *Portland Community College*

Tamie D. McCabe, *Redlands Community College*

Terry Reeves, *Red Rocks Community College*

Matt B. Roscoe, *The University of Montana*

Karen Walters, *Arapahoe Community College*

It is also important to know that you have a very valuable resource available to you in your Pearson Addison-Wesley sales representative. If you do not know your representative, you can locate him/her by logging on to www.aw.com/replocator and typing in your zip code. Please feel free to contact your representative if you have any questions relating to our text or if you need additional supplements. Of course, you can always contact us directly at math@aw.com.

 In addition, the Addison-Wesley Math Adjunct Support Center, staffed by qualified mathematics instructors with over 50 years of combined experience at both the community college and university level, provides assistance for faculty. Support is provided in the areas of suggested syllabus consultation, tips on using materials packaged with your book, book-specific content assistance, and teaching suggestions including advice on classroom strategies. For more information, visit www.aw-bc.com/tutorcenter/math-adjunct.html.

We know that teaching this course can be challenging. We hope that this and the other resources we have provided will help to minimize the amount of time it takes you to meet those challenges.

Good luck in your endeavors!

The Bittinger/Ellenbogen/Johnson book team

Dear Adjunct Faculty and Mentors:

My purpose in writing this introduction is to encourage all faculty, in particular adjunct instructors and those responsible for guiding them, to use the Instructor and Adjunct Support Manual. Adjunct faculty are playing an increasingly larger role in colleges and universities. At my institution adjunct faculty teach over 50% of the mathematics courses. In addition the adjunct's job is more challenging today than ever before. Some are hired on very short notice. Many drive from school to school, leaving them with very little preparation time. Still others receive little or no mentoring. With this confluence of an expanded role and increased difficulties, there comes a growing need to provide adjunct faculty with the support materials to help them meet a variety of challenges. The Instructor and Adjunct Support Manual is an invaluable resource in this regard.

This supplement has been developed by instructors for instructors. Virtually every element of the manual is the result of thoughtful comments and suggestions from adjunct and full-time faculty and their mentors. The offered recommendations address the challenges and concerns that faculty experience. Proposed topics range from the practical, such as items to be included in a syllabus in Sample Syllabi, to the probing, such as the most effective way to teach a particular concept in Teaching Tips Correlated to Textbook Sections. Other topics include General, First-Time Advice, Extra Practice Exercises, and Helpful Tips for Using Supplements and Technology. As a result of faculty involvement, an extremely useful resource has been developed for all those engaged in the teaching experience.

Whether you are an adjunct instructor, a full-time faculty member, or a supervisor of adjunct faculty, I hope my words will motivate you to use the tools found in this support manual. Developed by teachers for teachers and dealing with a variety of pertinent topics, I believe you will find the Instructor and Adjunct Support Manual a wonderful addition to the support materials published by Pearson Addison-Wesley.Have a great semester!

John M. Samoylo
Mathematics Department Co-coordinator
Delaware County Community College

GENERAL, FIRST-TIME ADVICE

We asked the contributing professors for words of advice to instructors who are teaching this course for the first time or for the first time in a long while. Their responses can be found on the following pages.

Kandace Kling, *Portland Community College*

1. Plan ahead. Make a calendar for the entire quarter and follow it as much as possible. You want your students to be successful in their next class and this can't happen if you rush through the material at the end, or worse yet, don't make it to the material at the end.

2. Teach your students proper mathematics. Make sure you hold them accountable for proper notation. Students are better prepared to be successful if they do things right from the beginning. A lot of students try to get away with lazy documentation and say things like, "This is the way I think about it." I try to help them to understand that mathematics is a precise language and that there are proper ways to document their work.

3. Students need lots of practice. In addition to having students work on problems in groups or at the board in class, make sure that you assign a lot of practice problems for them to work at home and make sure that they understand how important it is for them to practice these problems. Students often tell me that it looks so easy when they watch me do the problems. I remind them that I spent years practicing.

4. Depending on the time constraints in your classroom, you may want to give homework quizzes each day that you meet or once a week to make sure that your students are keeping up with their practice problems. These can be short quizzes that make up a small percentage of their final grade. You may just give a half sheet quiz with a few problems or you may ask for them to do exact problems from the practice problem sets. If you ask for exact problems from the practice problem sets, make sure they do not have their books and don't tell them the problem. If you just tell them the section and the problem number, they can copy their work from their homework if they have it done. This is a quick way to find out who is keeping up with their homework.

5. Don't get discouraged. Make sure you talk to the people in your department who have been around for a while. They usually have great ideas and can give you great advice when you run into a problem.

Tamie D. McCabe, *Redlands Community College*

1. When I first began teaching, I was not as organized as I should have been. I felt like I was one section ahead of the students on how the book presented the material. Students didn't seem to read the text or, if they did, they were confused by what they read. I felt like I was behind where I should be in the text. So the next semester I created a notebook for myself that included sections on course content, chapter notes, chapter homework, tests, and projects. In the course content I included the syllabus and a calendar that charted what I needed to cover that day. I also did the homework assignment that I planned on assigning to ensure the problems fit what I covered and the assignment wasn't too lengthy, so the majority of the students wouldn't spend hours completing it. Then the next semester, to help the students become organized, I made them keep a notebook as well, with the hope that they would be better able to study this way.

2. I use the first day to go over the syllabus and give students some study tips. I stress the use of the study tips given in the book. To help them learn the terminology, I tell students to use 3×5 note cards to make flashcards. Additionally, I stress the use of the correct terminology in class.

3. When possible, I use PowerPoint presentations to show the list of steps and then the board and calculator to show examples.

4. I try to find examples in each chapter for all possible majors, so students can be aware of where they may use algebra.

5. I recommend that the students use the Student's Solution Manual.

Terry Reeves, *Red Rocks Community College*

1. As a way of getting to know my students and having them feel they can talk with me easily, I show up to class a few minutes early to chat with them. I pick something fun to open up the conversation, e.g., movies recently seen, current events, and the weekend's football games. At this level, students are generally still intimidated by math, so I try to create a relaxed atmosphere where students hopefully feel they can talk freely with me.

    Along the same lines, on the first day of class, I introduce myself and give some background information on myself. I then play a game where the students introduce themselves. The first student tells his/her name, major, and a good movie to recommend (or some other bit of information). The second students must announce the first student's name, then his/her own name, major and a good movie. The third student announces the names of the first two students, then his/ her own name, major, and a good movie. This goes on until we get to the last student (who usually doesn't want to be the last one called on!). No pencil and paper is allowed. I'm not usually big on these types of games, but this one is pretty fun, and it allows me to know everyone's name by the end of the first class. It also loosens up the students so that they begin talking to each other sooner rather than later.

2. We have prerequisites and entrance requirements to this class at my college, but sometimes these indicators still don't place students well. As an extra measure, on the first day I give students a short (about eight questions) assessment exam that tests them on key concepts from elementary algebra. This takes about 10–15 minutes; I tell the students a score of six or better is a good indicator that they are ready for this class. Anything below six, they should come and talk to me. This test doesn't mandate that they can't be in the class, but it does help encourage students to think about their placement. It also gives me the opportunity to do some informal advising so that I can help students decide if they are ready for this level.

3. During my lectures, I constantly ask students the next steps as I do examples on the board. This way, they are doing the problems instead of me. I just act as the note taker. For assessment purposes, this also helps me to know if I'm on track. If nobody can answer "What do we do next?" I then know that this is an area I need to talk about some more.

4. Volunteering in the math lab is an excellent way to help the tutors know what's being covered in your class and to help them with the important concepts students need to master. It also is an excellent way to gauge what areas students are struggling with before they are tested on the material.

Matt B. Roscoe, *The University of Montana*

1. First and foremost, welcome to the time-honored profession of teaching mathematics. Whether your time as an instructor of algebra is short-lived or life-long, you should know that you will be making a difference in the lives of your students. You will change how your students think and understand the world.

2. As a teacher, you are faced with the difficult question of how to best prepare your students for the challenges that face them in this course, in subsequent mathematics courses, and in life in general. I have found that a teacher is never *fully* prepared for lecture. Even after teaching the same intermediate algebra course over fifteen times, I am still changing my lecture notes and re-crafting my delivery. Think of your trade as a process which will evolve and perfect itself in time. Be patient. Leave room for improvement. Be prepared to laugh at yourself. View your failures as an opportunity for personal development.

3. Observe other teachers. I have found that this is the most effective means of perfecting your trade. Most of my instructional strategies are "borrowed" from other instructors that I have observed. Do not be afraid to experiment and try new methods of instruction. In addition to the traditional lecture, prepare in-class worksheets and try cooperative group-work. Be aware that there are many means by which you can achieve your instructional goals. Be creative.

4. Know that students are learning more than just mathematical content in your classroom. The *way* that you teach will affect your students. Be passionate about the content, its history, and how it has changed the way that we think and view the world. Find a lens to convey the necessity of mathematics to your

students. I like to tell stories about how certain discoveries where made; Pythagorus and the "unmentionable" irrationals, Galileo and the time-height polynomial, Cardano and imaginary numbers. As teachers of algebra we are in good company, historically speaking. These stories excite me and I believe that my passion for the saga of mathematics inspires my students. Determine what excites you and find a way to include it in your instruction. Your students will appreciate it and you will enjoy your work more fully.

Karen Walters, *Arapahoe Community College*

1. On the first day of class, I give a pretest similar to the final exam for the prerequisite class. This gives the students a good idea of their level of preparation for this class. I recommend that students with low scores either drop down to the prerequisite class or spend the first few weeks in intensive review of the prerequisite material. I also have the students fill out a questionnaire with contact information and information about their prior experience with mathematics. It helps to know how long it has been since their previous math class. For example, if it has been 10 years since a student has had a math class, they may do poorly on the pretest, but may be able to get up to speed quickly.

2. On the first day of class, I have the students exchange phone numbers and email addresses with the students sitting nearby. If students miss class and cannot reach me, they have several other students they can contact for notes and homework assignments. I encourage students to work together on their homework, and this exchange between the students on the first day often leads to the formation of study groups.

3. I include a grade calculation worksheet with my syllabus so that students can keep track of their grades. I explain to them how to calculate their grades so that they know how they are doing at any point in the semester.

4. I strongly recommend that you learn how to operate your calculator. Be very comfortable with the 2nd CALC functions as well as the regression calculations. You do not want to have to refer to notes or the book when a student asks you questions (and they will!). The book supports the TI-83 and TI-84 calculators, but students may have other calculators. You may want to specify in your syllabus which calculators you will support in class, and be sure that you are very familiar with all of them. If you do decide to allow calculators that you are not familiar with, require that your students bring their guidebooks to each class.

5. Every class period I have several students present problems from their homework on the board. They write up the solutions, showing all work, and then they explain their solutions to the class. This counts as part of their grade. They are reluctant at first, but after a couple of weeks they look forward to this and I sometimes have to limit their time at the board! This helps students with the extremely important objectives of writing and communicating mathematics.

6. Find examples that your students can relate to. Younger students may tune out if you are discussing mortgages, while returning students may not catch on to references about the latest CD or music television program. Students seem to pay more attention and have more fun in class if you include their names in your application problems.

7. When lecturing, come up with your own examples. Don't use the examples from the book. If you lecture straight from the textbook, students will not bother to read the book. Using your own examples gives the students another set of problems to use when they are preparing to do homework or studying for exams.

SAMPLE SYLLABI

Provided by:

Kandace Kling, *Portland Community College*

Tamie D. McCabe, *Redlands Community College*

Terry Reeves, *Red Rocks Community College*

Matt B. Roscoe, *The University of Montana*

Karen Walters, *Arapahoe Community College*

Portland Community College
P.O. Box 19000
Portland OR, 97280-0990

Classroom Course

Math 95   **Fall 2006**

INSTRUCTOR: Kandace Kling
OFFICE: ST 104
OFFICE HOURS: 10:30–11:00 WF
                     11:00–11:50 T Th
                     1:00–1:50 M W
OFFICE PHONE:
E-MAIL:
FAX:
WEB PAGE:
COURSE NUMBER & TITLE: MTH 95; Intermediate Algebra
COURSE SECTION NUMBER (CRN): 40284
ROOM: SCB 103
TIMES: 12:00–12:50, M–F

COURSE DESCRIPTION

MTH 95 is an intermediate algebra course that focuses on mathematical functions, as well as symbolic algebra skills needed for further course work in mathematics and science. Functions will be studied graphically, numerically and verbally as well as symbolically. Linear, quadratic and exponential functions will be explored in the context of applications.

PREREQUISITE

MTH 65 or MTH 70 and placement into WR 115

REQUIRED MATERIALS

Intermediate Algebra: Graphs and Models by Bittinger, Ellenbogen and Johnson, Addison-Wesley

Graphing calculator (A TI graphing calculator is recommended. The TI-92 and TI-86 will be used for demonstration in class. If you do not own a graphing calculator and are considering purchasing one, please discuss which calculator to purchase with the instructor.)

Graph paper (All graphs submitted for assessment must be made on graph paper. It is a very good idea to use graph paper for all graphs. Engineering paper is a bit expensive, but it is very useful for working on mathematics, engineering and science problems that include many graphs.)

ASSIGNED EXERCISES

A list of assigned exercises from the text will be distributed. Although your work on these exercises will not be assessed, it is expected that you have attempted, and hopefully completed, all these exercises. Some exam problems will be similar to assigned exercises. There are three distinct types of problems that have been assigned: drill-and-skill type problems, application problems and "synthesis" problems. The drill-and-skill type problems don't require a lot of thought, but require practice to master. I may have assigned too many or too few for your needs.

Traditionally, the application problems and synthesis problems come at the end of the problem sets. Their placement at the end of the section does not imply that these problems may be overlooked. The problems are more difficult because they are not as routine as the drill-and-skill problems. If you get bored or frustrated with the drill-and-skill problems, skip ahead to the application problems and synthesis problems (maybe after taking a break). The application problems are easy to identify; there is a lot of English and a minimal amount of symbols. The "synthesis" problems are identified by a separate sub-section of the problem sets. Fewer of these types of problems have been assigned; these problems require more thought. But these types of problems are no less important! You will see problems like these on worksheets and on exams (see below).

TESTING
There will be five tests and a comprehensive final exam. Test dates are given on the attached course calendar. **No make-up tests will be given.**

WORKSHEETS
Five worksheets will be collected during the term. I will count the top four in your final grade. Problem solutions will be assessed for presentation as well as for correctness. (See MTH 95 Documentation Guidelines.) **No late assignments will be accepted.** If you are unable to attend class on a day when an assignment is due, the assignment may be submitted by email, faxed (be sure to include my name on the fax) or dropped off in ST 104 by 4 P.M. on the due date. No exceptions.

CHEATING
This course outline incorporates PCC District Student Rights and Responsibilities including the Code of Student Conduct. First time cheating will result in exam failure. Second time cheating will result in course failure and may result in expulsion from PCC. Cheating during exams includes:
- discussing questions with anyone, except instructor or proctor;
- observing or attempting to observe exam papers or calculator screens of others;
- possessing crib notes or aids, including info stored in calculators; and
- possessing exams from prior course offerings.

EXPECTATIONS
You are expected to attend class and participate in class discussions and activities. You are expected to read the text; the first reading of a section or sections to be covered during a particular class meeting should be done before class. Assignments must be completed on time.

COURSE CALENDAR
A course calendar is attached to this syllabus. All dates are tentative and changes will be announced in class. It is your responsibility to keep track of any changes.

OUTSIDE HELP
I have regularly scheduled office hours; other times may be arranged by appointment. Please don't hesitate to see me for help with homework and calculator questions. However, ou may not see me for an "individualized" lecture over material you missed during a scheduled class. If you want information about activities which happened during a class you missed, you need to (kindly) ask a fellow (willing) student.
- There are math tutors available in CC 204A. These tutors are available five days a week. Visit the center for specific hours.
- Library—Web access
- Computer Resource Center (CC206)—EMIT
- Multicultural Center (CC202)—peer tutoring
- Writing Center (CC204B)
- Office for Students with Disabilities

Your best resource is your fellow students. You will be given ample opportunity to work with your fellow students in both lecture and lab; most students who extend these relationships outside of the classroom find that it enhances their learning of the material.

GRADING POLICY

Percentage Breakdown			Grade Requirements	
Test 1	15%		Grade	Min. Requirement
Test 2	15%	The top 4 grades	A	90%
Test 3	15%	will be taken	B	80%
Test 4	15%	from the five	C	70%
Test 5	15%	tests.	D	60%.
Worksheets	15%		F	
Final Exam	25%		Pass	70%
Total	100%		Audit	70% attendance

If you have a disability and need an accommodation, please make arrangements to meet with me outside of class. PCC students requesting accommodations must provide documentation of a disability and work with the Office for Students with Disabilities (OSD).

COURSE CALENDAR, Fall 2002

	Monday	Tuesday	Wednesday	Thursday	Friday
Week 1 9/23–9/27	Functions Section 2.1	Functions and Graph Reading Section 2.7	Review Linear Functions Section 2.4	Review Linear Functions Section 2.5	Review Linear Section 2.6 **WS 1 Due**
Week 2 9/30–10/4	Linear Inequalities Section 4.1	Compound Linear Inequalities Section 4.2	Absolute Value Equations Section 4.3	Absolute Value Inequalities Section 4.3	**TEST 1**
Week 3 10/7–10/11	Rational Expressions and Functions Section 6.1	Rational Expressions and Functions Section 6.2	Complex Rational Expressions Section 6.3	Rational Equations Section 6.4	Rational Expression and Equations **WS 2 Due**
Week 4 10/14–10/18	Applications and Models Section 6.5	Applications and Models Section 6.5	Formulas and Models Section 6.7	Formulas and Models Section 6.7	**TEST 2**
Week 5 10/21–10/25	Radicals Section 7.1	Rational Exponents Section 7.2	Simplifying Radical Expressions Section 7.3	Simplifying Radical Expressions Section 7.4	Simplifying Radical Expressions **WS 3 Due**
Week 6 10/28–11/1	Simplifying Radical Expressions Section 7.5	Inservice No Day Classes	Solving Radical Equations Section 7.6	Applications Section 7.7	**TEST 3**
Week 7 11/4–11/8	Complex Numbers Section 7.8	Review Quadratic Equations Section 8.1	Review Quadratic Equations Section 8.2	Review Quadratic Equations Section 8.3	Review Quadratic Section 8.4 **WS 4 Due**
Week 8 11/11–11/15	Variation and Problem Solving Section 8.5	Veteran's Day No Class	Introduction to Polynomial Section 5.1	Quadratic Functions Section 8.6	**TEST 4**
Week 9 11/18–11/22	Graphs of Quadratic Section 8.7	Applications of Quadratic Functions Section 8.8	Quadratic Functions	Introduction to Exponential Functions Section 9.1	Exponential Functions **WS 5 Due**

Week 10 11/25–11/29	Exponential Functions	Exponential Functions	TEST 5	Thanksgiving No Class	No class
Week 11 12/2–12/ 6	Solving Exponential Equations	Solving Exponential Equations	Base *e* and Inverse Functions	Base *e* and Inverse Functions	Review for Final Exam
Finals 12/9–12/13			FINAL EXAM 12:00–2:00		

SUGGESTED EXERCISES FROM THE TEXT

Notes on calculator usage: The directions in the text are explicit on calculator usage in some problems. For example, In Section 2.1, Problems 41–47, the text states, "Graph each function using a standard viewing window..." I expect that you will use a graphing calculator here. On the other hand, you may be tempted to use your calculator for some simple arithmetic problems. I will discourage calculator use here. (For example, see Footnote 3 for the Section 7.1 exercises.) Whenever a section included problems that ask you to match the symbolic representation of a function with its graph, I assigned these. On these problems try (try very hard) not to use a graphing calculator. You will be asked to do similar problems on quizzes and exams *without* a calculator. These exercises are not footnoted. See Section 2.4, Problem 37 as an example of this type of problem. If there is ever a question about appropriate calculator usage, please ask.

Week 1
Section 2.1: 1–35 odd, 41–47 odd, 55, 57[1]
Section 2.7: 1–23 odd, 25–27, 31, 35 a–e, 45, 53–58, 63, 73
Section 2.4: 1–21 every other odd, 25–30, 31–49 odd, 57, 61–69 odd, 89
Section 2.5: 1–21 every other odd, 23, 25, 39, 45, 55–63 odd, 65–77 every other odd
Section 2.6: 1, 5, 9, 13, 17, 19, 21, 31, 33, 35, 37, 39, 51, 55, 57, 59, 61, 63, 65

Week 2
Section 4.1: 1–11 odd, 13–49 every other odd, 51[2], 59, 63
Section 4.2: 1–9 odd, 11–35 every other odd, 37–61 every other odd, 63, 69, 87, 89
Section 4.3: 1–6, 7–31 odd, 39– 47 odd
Section 4.3: 49–59 odd, 67, 77, 79, 83, 87

Week 3
Section 6.1: 1–35 odd, 45–71 odd, 79, 80, 88, 91
Section 6.2: 1–45 every other odd, 52, 60–65
Section 6.3: 1–33 every other odd, 48, 51, 53–56
Section 6.4: 1–23 odd, 25, 31, 35, 51

Week 4
Section 6.5: 1, 5, 7, 15, 21, 27, 33, 37
Section 6.7: 1–25 odd, 28, 31, 36, 37–40

Week 5
Section 7.1: 1–17 odd[3], 23, 26, 29–53 every other odd, 57–63 odd, 77, 79, 95–98, 115
Section 7.2: 1–95 every other odd, 107, 111, 113
Section 7.3: 1–81 every other odd, 92–94
Section 7.4: 1–73 every other odd, 79

---
[1] You need to read the paragraph before both Problem 55 and Problem 57!
[2] Find a linear function to model the data algebraically. Do not use regression.
[3] No calculator on these problems!

Week 6
Section 7.5: 1–27 every other odd, 29, 33, 39–63 every other odd, 71, 74, 76, 79
Section 7.6: 1–17 every other odd, 37, 39, 45, 57, 58, 67
Section 7.7: 1, 9, 13, 15, 19 - 33, 45, 49, 57 - 67 odd

Week 7
Section 7.8: 1–85 every other odd, 97, 98
Section 8.1: 1–5 odd, 7–27 every other odd, 29–47 odd, 79
Section 8.2: 1–45 odd
Section 8.3: 1, 5, 15–31 odd, 33, 53
Section 8.4: 1, 5, 9, 13, 19, 23, 27, 33, 35–53 odd, 81

Week 8
Section 8.5: 1–49 every other odd, 57
Section 5.1: 1–6, 7–21 odd, 27, 29, 33, 35, 39–42, 43, 49, 51, 53–56, 98
Section 8.6: 1–12, 13, 15, 23–51 every other odd, 57–59, 61, 65, 69

Week 9
Section 8.7: 1–41 every other odd, 58
Section 8.8: 1, 7, 11, 13, 16–20, 21–27 odd, 32–33[4]
Section 9.1: 1–4, 5–23 odd, 35–40, 41–45 odd[5]

Weeks 10 and 11
Practice problems will be distributed in class.

DOCUMENTATION GUIDELINES
It is very important to document your work correctly when working an algebra problem. For this reason, I am going to ask you to be very precise about documenting your work. Always start by writing the original problem. When you are working a problem that requires several steps, record all of the terms in each step and line up your equal signs.

RULES OF THUMB
* A number, such as 5, all by its lonesome, is <u>not</u> a well-presented conclusion.
  Well-presented conclusions (depending on the type of problem):
  $f(2) = 2$
  $x = 5$

  The distance to the ballpark is 5 km.

* Equal signs must be used when changing the form of an expression.
  Well-presented factorization problem:
  $$3x^2 - 15x - 18 = 3(x^2 - 5x - 6)$$
  $$= 3(x - 6)(x + 1)$$

* Expressions on either side of an equal sign must be equivalent.
  $2x - 5 = 11$
  $2x - 5 = 11 + 5$ *Note: This line is a lie even though the student reached the correct conclusion!*
  $2x = 16$
  $x = 8$

---

[4] Do not use regression. Make a scatter plot and choose three points to use to determine the quadratic function.
[5] Make rough sketches of the functions that show whether the functions are increasing or decreasing and the value of the vertical intercepts. Be sure to label and scale the axes.

Correct presentation:
$$2x - 5 = 11$$
$$2x - 5 = 11 + 5$$
$$2x = 16$$
$$x = 8$$

The solution is 8. *Note: Equal signs need not be lined up when solving an equation.*

- When asked to simplify an expression, <u>always</u> start the presentation of the solution with the original expression (and line up the equal signs).

  Given $f(x) = 3x + 4$. Find and simplify $\dfrac{f(x + h) - f(x)}{h}$.

$$\dfrac{f(x + h) - f(x)}{h} = \dfrac{3(x + h) + 4 - (3x + 4)}{h} \quad \text{Note: This is the original expression}$$

$$= \dfrac{3x + 3h + 4 - 3x - 4}{h}$$

$$= \dfrac{3h}{h}$$

$$= 3$$

- Axes on graphs must be labeled and scaled. Otherwise the graph cannot be read and interpreted. Figure numbers and captions are always a good idea.

The volume of water in a tub

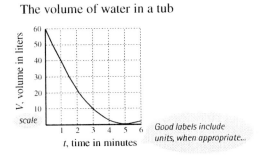

Good labels include units, when appropriate...

- When preparing work for submittal, the student should keep in mind that:
- all applications (story problems — example on back of this page) must be answered in complete sentences,
- illegible work will remain unmarked,
- ambiguous conclusions will be misinterpreted,
- analyses using improper notation and/or incomplete mathematical sentences will be rejected,
- solutions with incorrect units are incorrect solutions,
- undefined variables have no meaning, and
- graphs with unlabelled and/or unscaled axes have no meaning.

Example of a well-presented solution to an application problem

A car phone company offers two basic plans for the poor executive: plan A and plan B (*Note: This is the statement of the problem to be solved*). Plan A is a monthly service charge of $10, and a charge of 90¢ a minute for telephone air time; plan B is a monthly charge of $24, and a charge of 70¢ a minute for telephone air time. Create a mathematical model that describes each plan and use these models to estimate *when* one plan is better than the other.

$10 + .90(number of minutes) = total monthly charge for Plan A

$24 + .70(number of minutes) = total monthly charge for Plan B

Let n represent the number of minutes of telephone air time used in a month. (*Note: The variable is well defined*)

Then setting the total monthly charge for Plan A equal to the total monthly charge for plan B to find out how many minutes would cause the two plans to charge the same amount for a month, I obtain (*Note: This is an explanation of the problem-solving strategy*)

$$10 + .90n = 24 + .70n$$

Solving for n,

$$10 + .90n - .70n = 24 + .70n - .70n$$
$$10 + .20n = 24$$
$$10 - 10 + .20n = 24 - 10$$
$$.20n = 14$$
$$\frac{.20}{.20}n = \frac{14}{.20}$$
$$n = 70$$

Therefore, both plans charge the same amount if the telephone air time for the month is 70 minutes. Since Plan B has the higher monthly charge, Plan B will cost more if fewer than 70 minutes are used and Plan A will cost more if more than 70 minutes are used. In other words, Plan A is a better deal if less than 70 minutes are used and Plan B is a better deal if more than 70 minutes are used. (*Note: The conclusion is clear; correct units are included*)

Online WebCT Course

CRN: 31235   **Summer 2006**

INSTRUCTOR: Kandace Kling
OFFICE:
EMAIL: Please use WebCT mail.
WEBPAGE:
PREREQUISITES: Math 65 or Math 70 and placement into WR 115.
TEXTBOOK: *Intermediate Algebra: Graphs and Models*, 2nd Ed., Bittinger, Ellenbogen and Johnson.

REQUIRED MATERIALS

This is an online course, so you must have access to a computer that is connected to the Internet. In order to make sure that you view the correct formatting of the modules on WebCT, you should use **Internet Explorer version 6.0** (or "higher") as your browser. You will need **Microsoft Word with the Equation Editor or Math Type** so that you can submit homework containing proper mathematical symbols electronically. (If you want to use other software for homework assignments you will need to obtain permission from the instructor.) All MTH 95 classes at PCC require a graphing utility, and the TI-89 graphing calculator is officially recommended. Since you are interacting with this course via a computer, you are welcome to use computer software (like the free WinPlot for PC's) that enables you to graph algebraic functions and to perform calculations instead of a graphing calculator. (I should mention examinations will NOT be oriented to the calculator and it is therefore entirely possible to do very well in this class without a calculator. The main advantage to the graphing calculators comes during the investigation and discovery phase of the learning process, not during the assessment phase. While you are studying you should use your calculator to obtain graphs of functions and to check your solutions to practice problems. Not only will it help you better understand the mathematics by enabling you see it from another perspective, but it will also help you learn how to better drive your calculator - preparing you for future classes where the calculator will be used more often.)

COURSE DESCRIPTION

MTH 95 is an intermediate algebra course that focuses on mathematical functions, as well as symbolic algebra skills needed for further course work in mathematics and science. Quadratic, rational, radical and exponential expressions and functions will be explored graphically, numerically, verbally, and symbolically.

COURSE CALENDAR

For the most part, this course is organized by weeks. Each week starts on Monday and ends the following Monday. (So Mondays are both the first and last day of each week.) For each week a few modules on WebCT will be assigned, a list of appropriate practice problems from the textbook will be suggested, and one short quiz must be taken on WebCT. (There will be no quizzes during the week of the midterm or the last week of the quarter.)

In addition to these weekly activities, there will also be five worksheets (I will drop the lowest worksheet score), one mid-term exam, and one final exam. It is important that you keep track of the course calendar since it gives the weeks and dates of all course activities.

EXAMS
There will be one two-hour mid-term exam, as well as a cumulative final exam. The mid-term exam will be taken on Tuesday February 3 from 6 P.M.–8 P.M.. The final exam will be taken on Monday March 15 from 6 P.M.–8 P.M.. Your study of the material on WebCT and your practice of assigned exercises from the text will best prepare you for the exams. If the exam times are impossible for you, let me know and we can arrange an alternative time. *No make-up exams will be given unless requested (and allowed) at least a week before the exam date.* **Photo I.D. is required for both the mid-term and the final exam.**

QUIZZES
There will be eight short quizzes during the quarter, of which only seven will count towards your final grade (i.e., I will drop your lowest quiz score). There will be one quiz each week except for the week of the midterm and the last week of the quarter. The quizzes will be made available on Monday (the first day of each week) and must be taken by the following Monday (the last day of each week). Quizzes will consist of a few multiple-choice questions that you will answer on WebCT. You will be allowed one attempt at each quiz. Before attempting quizzes, study the modules assigned for that week and do the suggested practice problems from the textbook.

WORKSHEETS
During the quarter there will be five homework assignments, of which four will count towards your final grade (i.e., I will drop your lowest homework score); due dates are given in the course calendar. These assignments will be made available via WebCT in the Assignment Dropbox. You will need to answer these problems following the documentation guidelines (click here) and using **proper mathematical notation.** (Of course, two good guides for proper mathematical notion are the modules on WebCT and the examples in the textbook.) You will need to submit these homework assignments through WebCT in the Assignment Dropbox, so you will need to complete them electronically. The approved electronic media is **Microsoft Word with Equation Editor or Math Type.**

SUGGESTED PROBLEMS
For each module there is a list of problems from the textbook (given on the course calendar) that I *strongly* suggest you practice and study. The solutions to most of these problems can be found in the back of the textbook.

POINTS

Final Exam	200 points	
Mid–Term	150 points	
Homework	100 points	(4 at 25 points each)
Quizzes	84 points	(7 at 12 points each)
Total	**534 points**	

GRADES: **A:** 90–100%; **B:** 80–89%; **C:** 70–79%; **D:** 60–69%; **F:** below 60%

Instead of a letter grade, you may choose a Pass/No Pass grade or an Audit:
- You may opt for a grade of **PASS/NO PASS** (P/NP) for this course. (Consult your advisor to determine if PASS/NO PASS is allowed for your major.) Requests for PASS/NO PASS shall be made in a WebCT "private mail" email to the instructor on or before the day of the final exam. You must receive a final course grade of C or better to receive a PASS.
- An **AUDIT** (AUD) is allowed if you attend at least two-thirds of the class meetings. Requests for an AUDIT must be submitted in a WebCT "private mail" email to instructor on or before the day of the final exam. Requests will be granted at the instructor's discretion.

EXTRA HELP

I will do my best to answer all questions sent to me via the WebCT email, but I will not be available 24/7. Please try to be patient. You can also get lots of great help from your classmates. One of the best ways to learn is to hear the questions other students have and to either answer the questions or listen to how other students answer the questions. In other words, having a dialogue about what you're trying to learn can greatly improve your understanding. So I sincerely hope that you will utilize the **Discussion Board**. It's one of the best features of WebCT, so take advantage of it!

If you would like to come to campus for help, The Math Center (CC 204A) and The Multicultural Center (CC 202) have math tutors. These are great places to study since there are tutors there to help if you get stuck. The Math Center is open Monday–Thursday from 9 A.M. to 8 P.M. and on Friday from 9 A.M. to 2 P.M.. You'll have to contact The Multicultural Center to find out when math tutors are available.

ADA STATEMENT

If you have a disability and need an accommodation, please let me know at the beginning of the quarter so that we can make arrangements. PCC students requesting accommodations must provide documentation of disability and work with the Office for Students with Disabilities (OSD) in ST 229.

MATH 0123 — Intermediate Algebra

Redlands Community College
Fall 2006 3 Credit Hours

Instructor:	Tamie D. McCabe
Telephone Number:	
Fax:	
E-Mail:	
Office:	MM - 211 (Located inside MM - 210)
Office Hours:	MWF 9:00 A.M.–10:00 A.M.; 2:00 P.M.–3:30 P.M., TTh by appointment.
Class Meeting Time:	Monday, Wednesday 5:30 P.M. to 6:45 P.M.
Class Room:	MM 214

COURSE DESCRIPTION

Intermediate Algebra is the second course in the process of learning algebra. This course presents absolute value, linear equations, graphing, rational expressions and equations, concept of function, systems of equations, exponents, quadratic equations and inequalities.

RATIONALE

Skills in algebra enable the student to open many more doors that might not otherwise be available. The skills aid in furthering the student's collegiate education. If the student has an adequate mastery of algebraic skills, he or she can use them in everyday life as well, i.e. calculating taxes, mortgage payments, critical thinking, et cetera.

PREREQUISITES

A satisfactory placement score, or pass MATH 0113: Basic Algebra with a grade of "C" or higher.

NEXT COURSE

Either MATH 1493 – Contemporary Mathematics or MATH 1513 – College Algebra. Please see an advisor for appropriate placement.

REQUIRED MATERIALS

Intermediate Algebra: Graphs and Models (2nd edition) Addison Wesley (Bittinger, Ellenbogen, Johnson)

RECOMMENDED MATERIALS

- *Student's Solutions Manual* (2nd edition) Addison Wesley (Bittinger, Ellenbogen, Johnson)
- Graphing Calculator (TI-83 recommended) and instruction booklet.

COURSE OBJECTIVES

This course provides the student with the algebraic skills necessary to continue on to College Algebra, where more complex equations will be introduced and the student should be able to apply the skills learned in this course to those more complex situations. Students completing this course should have knowledge of mathematical terminology in relationship to algebra. Students should be able to apply the skills and techniques learned to solve everyday problems which helps to develop problem-solving skills and foster critical thinking within a varied setting.

COURSE MEASURE

Any student completing this class should be able to perform the following skills and techniques, without references, unless otherwise stated, and to the degree of satisfaction listed in the grading section of this syllabus.

- Evaluate, simplify, solve, write and sketch linear equations and inequalities that involve ratios, proportions, rates percent, and absolute value.
- Perform the four basic arithmetic operations on polynomials. Evaluate, simplify, solve, write and polynomials.
- Perform the four basic arithmetic operations on rational expressions and solve these expressions.
- Evaluate, simplify, solve and write equations involving radicals and complex numbers. Perform the four basic arithmetic operations on expressions that involve radicals or complex numbers.
- Evaluate, simplify, solve and write quadratic equations or inequality. Determine the number and type of solutions of a quadratic equation. Sketch the graph of a quadratic inequality.
- Determine and plot solution points of equations. Find the distance between two points in a plane. Determine the slope of a line. Graph a line. Write the equation of a line.
- Evaluate and sketch the graph of a function. Find the Domain and the inverse.
- Solve systems of equations.

GOALS AND COMPETENCIES FOR STUDENT SUCCESS

Addressed in this course are: solving problems critically by identifying the problem defining a problem, collecting data, analyzing and interpreting data, formulating conclusions, generating possible solutions and evaluating solutions.

COURSE CONTENT/SCHEDULE

Following is a *tentative* schedule of course events and is subjected to change without notice.

Content To Be Covered

Chapter R:	Elementary Algebra Review	Sections 1–6
Chapter 7:	Rational Expressions, Equations, and Functions	Sections 1–8
Chapter 8:	Systems of Linear Equations and Problem Solving	Sections 1–5, 9
Chapter 9:	Exponents and Radical Functions	Sections 1–9
Chapter 10:	Quadratic Functions and Equations	Sections 1–9

Special Events	**Date**
Last Day to Drop THIS Course	September 1, 2006
Labor Day (Campus Closed)	September 4, 2006
Fall Break (Campus Closed	October 19–20, 2006
Last Day to Withdraw	November 10, 2006
Thanksgiving Break (Campus Closed)	November 22–24, 2006

COURSE WORK

- Textbook Reading and Online Supplements: Students are expected to complete the reading assignments, as directed by the instructor. Online supplements, available through My Math Lab, http://www.mymathlab.com, maybe used by the students.
- Quizzes: Brief quizzes are assigned periodically throughout the course and due on dates to be determined by the instructor. Each quiz is worth 10 points.

- Homework: Homework will be assigned at the end of each class period. Homework will be collected and graded at the instructor's discretion (usually every class period). Each homework assignment is worth 100 points. In order to receive credit for the homework, students must show their work, and the work must fit with the problem. DO NOT USE SPIRAL PAPER. **NO late homework will be accepted.** You may drop your two lowest homework papers. See handout for specific homework layout details.

- Exams 1, 2, 3, 4, and 5: Chapter Exams, each covering approximately one chapter, will be worth 100 points each. Tests are closed-book and closed notes unless otherwise instructed. Calculators may be used on your exam. The lowest chapter exam will be dropped. Problems on tests are graded giving partial credit, therefore, the student should show all of his/her work on problems enabling me to ascertain the procedures used that deserve credit. No partial credit will be given on multiple-choice questions. Recommended resources for use during the exams is a graphing calculator.

- Final Exam: The final exam will be taken in class during the last week of classes. All students will be required to take the final exam. This exam will be worth 120 points and covers Chapter R and Chapters 7–10. Students will be able to use a graphing calculator.

COURSE EVALUATION

The course grade will be assigned according to the following scale based on the number of total points.

	Grade	Points
A	90–100 %	720–648 Points
B	80–89 %	647–576 Points
C	70–79 %	575–504 Points
D*	60–69 %	503–432 Points
F*	Below 60 %	Below 432 Points

* It is strongly recommended that the student retake the course.

* **NOTE:** Students who earn the grade of **AW**, **W**, or **F** in a 0-level class may repeat the course one time. This also applies to students enrolled prior to Fall 2005.

COURSE POLICIES

- **Cell Phones, Pagers, and Alarm Devices:** All cell phones, pagers, any other alarm or ringing devices must be turned off while in Class.

- **Food and Drinks:** No food allowed in the classroom.

- **North Lab Policy:** You MUST show a photo ID and provided your own pencil or pen to use. The back of your calculator must be taken off and placed on the selves along with any books. Students may not share calculators or use their cell phone as a calculator on exams. Scratch paper may not be used unless the instructor as attached it to the back of the exam and must be turned in with the exam. Cell phones must be turned off. No food, drinks or children are allowed in the Testing Center. Failure to follow the above could result in the student being unable to test in the testing center.

- **Withdrawal:** You may drop the class without obtaining signatures through June 9, 2006; you will no be charged for the class, and the class will not appear on your transcript. You may withdraw from the class through July 14, 2006, but you must have the instructor's signature; you will be charged for the class, and the class will appear on your transcript. YOU MAY NOT WITHDRAW FROM THE CLASS AFTER JULY 14, 2006.

- **Academic dishonesty:** Academic dishonesty is not condoned or tolerated. Academic dishonesty, is behavior in which a deliberately fraudulent misrepresentation is employed in an attempt to gain undeserved intellectual credit, either for one's self or another. The minimum penalty for an act of academic dishonesty will be a grade of "0" on the exam, quiz or homework in question.

- **Accommodations for Students with Special Needs:** Redlands Community College complies with Section 504 of the Rehabilitation Act of 1973 and the Americans with Disabilities Act of 1990. Students with disabilities who need special accommodations should make their requests in the following way: (1) talk with your instructor after class or during office hours about your disability or special need related to work in the class; and/or (2) contact Student Support Services and ask to speak to the ADA officer.

I acknowledge by signing below that I have received the syllabus for the course:

_____
(List Course Here)

I have reviewed the syllabus and understand the objectives of this course. I understand, further, how my performance will be evaluated and how my final grade will be determined. I am aware of my instructor's office hours and I know how to contact him/her for help with and/or clarification of course content or procedures.

_____   _____
(Student Signature)   (Date)

Syllabus for Mat 106 - Survey of Algebra

Instructor Contact Information
Instructor: Ms. Terry Reeves (please address me as Terry)
Email:
Telephone:
Office: Room 2618
Office hours: 10–11 A.M. MW and 1–2 P.M. TTh

Course Description
Description: Survey of Algebra (also known as Intermediate Algebra) is the prerequisite for College Algebra, Introduction to Statistics, Math for the Liberal Arts, and Math for Elementary Teachers. Topics for this course include: algebra basics, functions, linear equations, graphs, inequalities, rational equations, exponents, radicals and quadratic equations.

Prerequisite: Beginning Algebra (Mat 090) with a grade of C or better. Also, you must have on the first day, the technology and the skills to operate a computer, perform word processing, and have the ability to send and receive E-mail.

Course Materials
Text: *Intermediate Algebra: Graphs and Models*, 2nd Edition, by Bittinger & Ellenbogen & Johnson, Addison Wesley.

Requirements: A scientific calculator will be required for the course.

Besides a working computer, you must also have a calculator. If you do not already have one and you plan to take Mat 121 (College Algebra) a TI-83 series calculator is your best choice.

CourseCompass Technical Support Line: 1-800-677-6337 or E-mail them at support

Grading
Assessment, Evaluation and Grading Policies
Your grade will be based upon three different items:
- (800 points) 8 unit exams worth 100 points each (exams are found under 'Course Material').
- (240 points) 8 quizzes worth 30 points each (quizzes are also found under 'Course Material'.
- (80 possible points) At least 16 Threaded Discussions responses (2 separate responses for each unit) worth 5 points each. You must make meaningful contributions to the discussion to receive full credit for the topic (discussions are found .

This gives a total of 1120 points. Your final grade will be based upon these points.

A	90–100 %
B	80–89 %
C	70–79 %
D	60–69 %
F	0–59 %

Your grade is based upon these points only. Please do not ask for extra credit beyond what is mentioned in this course. Whatever is offered to one student must be offered to all students for fairness (and for legal considerations also.) If circumstances make it difficult for you to keep up with the course, then drop it and take it at a time when the situation has improved.

Going Online: Students may log on and off as often as they wish and at any time. However, to be successful in this format it is imperative that you not get behind. Active communication with me (and preferably, also your classmates) is also imperative to succeed in this course. Please note that this course is NOT a self-paced course. Each unit has a due date; late work will not be accepted without prior consent from me.

The only work which is required to be "turned in" for each unit is your responses to the threaded discussions, quizzes, and the unit exam. Failure to complete the threaded discussion, quiz, and exam by the due date (without prior consent) will result in an automatic zero for any unsubmitted work.

If you have questions or concerns, you may E-mail me at any time. I will make every effort to return your E-mail with 48 hours or less (Monday-Friday only). During the weekdays, I am usually able to return a phone call or E-mail within 24 hours (but, no guarantee). Any exceptions to the 48-hour response time will be communicated during the course.

Exams: Every chapter has an exam with approximately 20 questions to be taken on the computer through the exam link in each unit. The exams must be taken by the deadline given in the syllabus. DO NOT WAIT UNTIL THE LAST MINUTE TO TAKE AN EXAM. Each exam is over the objectives for that chapter. For the exam, you may use your textbook and notes, but another person is not allowed to help you, nor are you to help anyone else. The exam is to be your own work. You will have three hours to take the exam which is more than enough time if you are well-prepared. Otherwise, you will run out of time. **This three hours must be done in one sitting.** If you are kicked out of an exam before you are finished, re-enter the exam immediately (the clock keeps running.)

The computer will attempt to give you a grade at after you have submitted your exam. I will re-grade your exam before determining your final test grade. Therefore, do not assume that the grade the "computer" gives you immediately after you take an exam is your final exam score. I will post your score in the grade book after looking over your exam.

The CourseCompass website has practice tests, study plans, and a tutorial center to help you. Take advantage of these resources as you need them.

Threaded Discussions: You will be required to make meaningful contributions to the threaded discussion. A discussion topic will be posted for all to read and respond to. Meaningful contributions include but are not limited to making intelligent and polite comments related to the topic, answering questions posed by other students, and asking related questions for others to consider. Chapter assignments may need to be done prior to entering the discussions. Each unit will have a total of ten points for the threaded discussion area. *Two responses, each worth five points, are required for each unit (you may respond more).* Ideally, I would like to see at least one response to the threaded discussion topic, and at least one response to a classmate's response. Do not feel pressured to have the "right" answer in order to participate in the thread; good questions and thoughtful comments are welcome and encouraged. In order to have the most benefit to the class, responses to the threaded discussion will be due before the last day of each unit

Homework: Homework assignments may be found under the "Assignments" link for each unit. The homework assigned in this course does not need to be turned in. However, it is to your benefit to do the homework and I will be happy to look over any homework you Email, mail, fax, or drop off with me. You may choose to do more or less than what is assigned. How much homework you choose to do should depend upon your understanding of the material. If you choose not to do any of the homework, chances are excellent that you will not learn the material and hence, not do well for the course.

If you have specific homework questions, or have general questions connected with the course, feel free contact me via E-mail. I will answer your questions within a day or two.

The tests each contain 20 questions worth 5 pts. each. Please study and do HW and quizzes before attempting each test. You will have 180 minutes for each test. This is ample time to complete each test and check your answers if you are proepared. At the end of 180 minutes, the test will automatically end, so once you start, you need to finish (i.e., you will not be permitted to log in a second time to finish the test). For online testing, do not copy work or have others help you or do the work for you. You are responsible to learn the matieral and ultimately, to show what you have learned. Late quizzes, exams, or required threaded responses will not be accepted without prior consent.

Course Due Dates:

NOTE: all due dates are active until Midnight (Mountain time zone) of the due date:

Unit 1: Chapter 1 (sec. 1.1–1.7)

Quiz, covers sec. 1.1–1.4	8/28/06
Unit 1 required thread	9/01/06
Exam 1	9/03/06

Unit 2: Chapter 2 (sec. 2.1–2.6)

Unit 2 required thread	9/10/06
Exam 2	9/12/06

Unit 3: Chapter 3 (sec. 3.1–3.5)

Quiz, covers sec. 3.1-3.3	9/18/06
Unit 3 required thread	9/20/06
Exam 3	9/22/06

Unit 4: Chapter 4 (sec. 4.1–4.4)

Unit 4 required thread	9/29/06
Exam 4	10/01/06

Unit 5: Chapter 5 (sec. 5.1–5.8)

Quiz A, covers sec. 5.1–5.4	10/09/06
Quiz B, covers sec. 5.5–5.8	10/17/06
Unit 5 required thread	10/18/06
Exam 5	10/20/06

Unit 6: Chapter 6 (sec. 6.1–6.8)

Quiz, covers sec. 6.1–6.4	10/28/06
Unit 6 required thread	11/03/06
Exam 6	11/05/06

Unit 7: Chapter 7 (sec. 7.1–7.8)

Quiz, covers sec. 7.1–7.4	11/13/06
Unit 7 required thread	11/18/06
Exam 7	11/20/06

Unit 8: Chapter 8 (sec. 8.1–8.9)

Quiz A, covers sec. 8.1–8.4	11/28/06
Quiz B, covers sec. 8.5–8.8	12/05/06
Unit 8 required thread	12/05/06
Exam 8	12/07/06

You are allowed to work ahead, but you are expected to meet (or beat) each deadline.

Note: Grades of "AW" will not be given in this course.

Extra Help: The LaRC (Learning and Resource Center) is an excellent place to get help in doing HW (at RRCC Lakewood and Arvada campuses). For hours, please call the Lakewood campus or the Arvada campus. Please take advantage of this opportunity for extra help.

Important Dates: 9/06/06—Last day to drop 15 week classes and initiate a tuition refund 11/14/06—Last day to withdraw from 15-week classes

Last, remember that I am here to help you learn the material. I hope to see many of you during my office hours. If you can't make my office hours, E-mail or voice mail is always encouraged. I will make every attempt to return messages within 24 hours during the weekdays.

Note: Any changes to the syllabus will be announced to the class via E-mail. Please make sure that your instructor has a current E-mail address for you.

Suggested Homework Assignments

Survey of Algebra suggested HW:

CHAPTER 1

sec. 1.1, pg. 11: (1–75) odd

sec. 1.2, pg. 22: (1–11) odd, 17, 19, 21, 25, 29, 31, (35–155) multiples of 5, 157,158–160

sec. 1.3, pg. 30: 1–10, 11, 15, 17, 21,(30–80) multiples of 5, (85–91) odd, 95–96

sec. 1.4, pg. 39: (1–37) odd, 41, 42

sec. 1.5, pg. 47: (1–45) every other odd, 47, 49, 53, 65, 67, 71, 72

sec. 1.6, pg. 58: (1–109) every other odd, 115, 117, 121–124

sec. 1.7, pg. 66: (1–67) odd, 69,72

CHAPTER 2

sec. 2.1, pg. 82: 1–6, (7–57) odd, (59–65) odd

sec. 2.2, pg. 93: (1–41) odd, 43, 45, 47, 51, 53, 55, 57, 61, (71–79) odd

sec. 2.3, pg. 107: 1–6, 9, 11, 15, 21, (23–96) every other odd

sec. 2.4, pg. 121: 1–10, 13, 17, 21, (27–37) odd, 43, 51, 53, 57, 61, 65, 67, 71, 75, 81, 83, 85, 87–93

sec. 2.5, pg. 129: 1–10, 15, 19, 23, 27, 31, 35, 37, 41, 49, 53, 57, 59, 61, (63–97) odd

sec. 2.6, pg. 139: 1–6 (7–29) every other odd, 35–40, (41–76) every other odd

CHAPTER 3

sec. 3.1, pg. 156: 1–8, 11, 13, 15, 19, 23, 33, (41–55) odd, 57–62

sec. 3.2, pg. 165: 1–6, 9, 11, 13, 15, 21, 27, 33, 39, 45, 49, 57–62

sec. 3.3, pg. 177: (1–17) every other odd, (19–44) odd, 51–55

sec. 3.4, pg. 187: 1–8, 9, 11, 15, 17, 21, 23, 29, 35, 41–45

sec. 3.5, pg. 193: (1–25) every other odd, 27–33

CHAPTER 4

sec. 4.1, pg. 230: 1–10 13, 15, 19, 27, 43, 47, 51, 55, 61, 69, 75, 79–87

sec. 4.2, pg. 241: 1–10, 14, 17, 21, 27, 31, 39, 43, 49, 53, 55, 59, 65, 67, (73–81) odd, 85–89

sec. 4.3, pg. 251: 1–8, 11, 19, 27, 31, 41, 43, 49, 59, 67, 77, 85, 91, 93–97

sec. 4.4, pg. 262: 1–6, 7, 9, 13, 17, 25, 27, 31, 33, 39, 43, 47, 51, 59–63

CHAPTER 5

sec. 5.1, pg. 285: 1–10, 11, 15, 19, 21, 25, 27, 21, (35–57) odd, 61, 67, 71, 75, 79, 83, 87, 91, 95, 99–103

sec. 5.2, pg. 298: 1–8, 13, 21, 27, 31, 39, 47, 57, 69, 75, 77, 81, 83–88

sec. 5.3, pg. 306: (1–69) every other odd, 71–76

sec. 5.4, pg. 317: (1–85) every other odd, 89–94

sec. 5.5, pg. 323: 1–10 15, 21, 27, 37, 41, 43, 47, 51, 53, 57, 59, 63, 71, 75–82

sec. 5.6, pg. 328: 1–10, 11, 19, 27, 33, 41, 43, 49–44

sec. 5.7, pg. 333: 1–6, 7, 17, 25, 31, 37, 43, 47, 51, 55–60

sec. 5.8, pg. 342: 1–6, 9, 19, 25, 29, 37, 39, (41–71) every other odd, 73–104

CHAPTER 6

sec. 6.1, pg. 360: 1–10 all, 11, 15, 19, 27, 35, 41, 49, 53, 57, 61, 69, 73,77,81, 87–92

sec. 6.2, pg. 370: 1–8, (9–70) every other odd, 71, 73–78

sec. 6.3, pg. 380: 1–6, (7–49) every other odd, 53–58

sec. 6.4, pg. 388: 1–10 all, 15, 19, 23, 27, 31, 33, 35, 39, 43, 45, 47, 53–58

sec. 6.5, pg. 397: (1–37) every other odd, 41–46

sec. 6.6, pg. 405: 1–6 11, 15, 19, 27, 29, 33, 39, 43, 47–53

sec. 6.7, pg. 411: 1–8 all, 11, 13, 17, 21, 25, 31–36

sec. 6.8, pg. 420: 1–10, (11–39) odd, (41–81) every other odd, 83–98

CHAPTER 7

sec. 7.1, pg. 443: 1–8, 11, 15, 17, 25, 27, 31, 35, 41, 47, 53, 57, 61, 65, 71, 73, 81, (87–103) odd, 107–112

sec. 7.2, pg. 449: 1–8, 9, 21, 25, 29, 33, 39, 43, 47, 53, 55, 59, 67, 71, 75, 79, 87, 93, 99, 101–106

sec. 7.3, pg. 457: 1–6, 11, 17, 23, 33, 37, 39, 41, 45, 47, 51, 55, 59, 63, 69, 73, 79–84

sec. 7.4, pg. 465: 1–8, (9–73) odd, 75–80

sec. 7.5, pg. 472: 1–6, 9, 13, 15, 19, 23, 25, 29, 35, 41, 45, 49, 51, 55, 59, 67, 75, 79, 83, 91, 95, 97, 99, 101, 105, 107, 113–118

sec. 7.6, pg. 479: 1–6, (7–45) every other odd, 53, 57–62

sec. 7.7, pg. 487: 1–6, 9, 15, 17, (21–49) odd, 53–58

sec. 7.8, pg. 497: 1–8, 9, 15, 21, 27, 29, 33, 39, 45, 47, 51, 67, 71, 77, (81–95) odd, 99–104

CHAPTER 8

sec. 8.1, pg. 515: 1–6, (7–23) odd, 27, 37, 43, 47, 51, 59, 65, 70, 75, 77–82

sec. 8.2, pg. 512: 1–6, (7–35) every other odd, 37, 39, 41, 43, 47, 51–56

sec. 8.3, pg. 528: (1–41) every other odd, 45–50

sec. 8.4, pg. 535: 1–6, 7, 13, 17, 21, 26, 31, 35, 41, 45, 49, 53, 59–64

sec. 8.5, pg. 541: 1–8, (9–41) every other odd, 45–50

sec. 8.6, pg. 549: 1–8, (9–57) every other odd, 61–66

sec. 8.7, pg. 556: 1–8, 11, 15, 17, 21, 25, 31, 37, 39, 41, 43, 44, 45–50

sec. 8.8, pg. 563: 1–6, (7–39) every other odd, 45–50

sec. 8.9, pg. 576: 1–8, (9–45) every other odd, 49–54

COURSE GUIDE
MATH 100 — INTERMEDIATE ALGEBRA
THE UNIVERSITY OF MONTANA
Spring 2007

INTRODUCTION

MATH 100 - Intermediate Algebra is offered for students who need to improve their algebra skills before entering college level mathematics courses. MATH 100 is intended for students who have not yet mastered a second year of high school algebra as well as for those who need a refresher course. MATH 100 does not substitute for any other mathematics requirement nor does it fulfill the general education mathematics requirement, however, credit is allowed toward graduation and grade point average. Unless a student has prior written approval by the Department of Mathematical Sciences, credit is not allowed for MATH 100 if it has been or is being earned in any mathematics course numbered above 100. Placement in MATH 100 is based on your individual mathematics assessment through the university placement exam, ACT/SAT math score, or successful completion of MAT 005 - Introductory Algebra. *It is crucial that you enroll in the proper math class at the beginning of the semester. If you have any concerns about your placement see your instructor immediately.*

LEARNING OUTCOMES

Upon successful completion of the course, students will be able to perform each of the following:
1.   Solve linear equations and inequalities in one variable
2.   Graph and describe the solutions linear equations and inequalities in two variables
3.   Solve systems of linear equations and inequalities in two variables
4.   Operate with polynomial expressions, solve integer factorable polynomial equations
5.   Operate with rational expressions, solve rational equations
6.   Operate with natural, integer, and rational exponents
7.   Operate with complex numbers
8.   Solve quadratic equations that are not integer factorable
9.   Graph quadratic equations, find vertices
10.   Solve exponential equations in one variable using a logarithm
11.   Graph and describe the solutions to exponential and logarithmic equations in two variables
12.   Model application problems using the skills listed above
13.   Apply calculator technology as an aid to problem solving in algebra

METHOD OF INSTRUCTION

MATH 100 is a lecture-lab course. Students are expected to attend three lectures and two hours of lab time each week. Each lecture will present concepts and example problems for each section of the text according to the course schedule. Weekly lab exercises will take place in the Mathematics Learning Center (MLC) located in Room 3 in the basement of the Mathematics Building. The MLC is open Monday through Friday, 8:00 A.M.–5:00 P.M.. Students are responsible for self scheduling two hours of lab time each week in the MLC to complete and submit the weekly laboratory exercises. In addition to lecture and lab, 10–15 hours of study and homework practice are usually required for successful completion of the course.

GRAPHING CALCULATOR

A graphing calculator is required for the course. The Texas Instruments TI-83 is the preferred calculator for the course and will be featured in classroom demonstrations. The TI-82 and TI-84 are also acceptable. Calculators with symbolic manipulation capabilities (e.g. TI-89, TI-92) will not be allowed in testing situations.

COURSE WEBSITE

http://web.math.umt.edu/roscoe/math100

The course website contains:

- **Laboratory Exercises:** Each student is expected to complete the weekly lab exercise that is available in the Mathematics Learning Center (MLC). Exercises will be available at 8:00 A.M. Monday and must be completed and submitted to an assistant in the MLC by Friday at 5:00 P.M. to receive credit. Exercises complement the weekly course topics and give the student an opportunity to demonstrate their knowledge outside of the exam setting. The ten highest lab exercise scores will be averaged at the end of the semester. Laboratory exercises will not be accepted late. No exceptions.

- **Homework/Quizzes:** Individual homework policies are determined by each instructor.

- **Midterm exams:** The two midterm exams are given in class. Graphing calculators removed from their cases are permitted but may not be shared with other students during the exam. Graphing calculators that are capable of symbolic manipulation such as the TI-89 or the TI-92 will not be allowed in testing situations. All scratch work must be done directly on the exam and returned to the instructor when leaving the classroom. Notes, guides, or cheat sheets are not allowed. All students must practice academic honesty as defined by the Student Conduct Code which is available for review online at http://www.umt.edu/SA/VPSA/index.cfm/page/1321. Academic misconduct is subject to an academic penalty by the course instructor and a disciplinary sanction by the university. When extenuating circumstances prevent a student from taking an exam at the scheduled time, the student must contact the instructor **PRIOR** to the time of the exam to announce their absence. Absences are excused only for reasons of illness, injury, family emergency, or a University sponsored activity. Arrangements for a make-up exam must occur within a week of the scheduled exam date. Failure to arrange a make-up exam within a week of the scheduled exam date will result in a score of zero for the exam.

- **Comprehensive Final:** The final exam is comprehensive. The final exam for Math 100 is given during the final examination week. See the official Class Schedule for the date and time of the final exam. The date and time of the final exam cannot be changed.

GRADING POLICIES

Math 100 can be taken for a traditional letter grade only. Math 100 cannot be taken credit/no credit. Grades will be determined according to the following distribution:

Laboratory Exercises	100
Homework	100
Midterm Exam #1	100
Midterm Exam #2	100
Midterm Exam #3	100
Comprehensive Final	200
Total Points Possible	**700**

The letter grade percent intervals for the course are as follows:

F	0–59
D–	60–62
D	63–67
D+	68–69
C–	70–72
C	73–77
C+	78–79
B–	80–82
B	83–87
B+	88–89
A–	90–92
A	93–100

PETITIONS FOR LATE WITHDRAWAL AND INCOMPLETES

Student election for withdrawal from Math 100 can occur up to the 30th day of instruction. After the 30th day of instruction petitions for late withdrawal will be considered only for students who demonstrate one of the university approved excuses:

1. Error in registration
2. Accident or illness
3. Family emergency
4. Change in work schedule

A grade of incomplete will only be considered when all three of the following are true:

1. The student has been in regular attendance and passing up to three weeks before the end of the academic semester
2. The instructor and the student agree that there is a reasonable probability that the student will be able to make-up the work required to complete the course and specific arrangements are drawn up and signed by both

When a student receives an incomplete the student has one calendar year to resolve the incomplete (I) before it automatically reverts to a failing grade (F).

SUGGESTED HOMEWORK

Section	Homework Problems	Section	Homework Problems
1.1	25–42, 59–62	6.1	13–56, 61–70
1.2	119–132, 141–156	6.2	9–54
1.3	17–26, 59–84	6.3	7–35
1.4	4–10, 19–30	6.4	11–40, 47–52
1.5	9–26	6.5	7–16, 23–26, 31–36
1.6	11–32, 73–110	7.1	31–104
1.7	7–38	7.2	9–98
2.1	13–36, 37–58	7.3	7–20, 27–40, 57–68
2.2	9–16, 21–42	7.4	1–20, 27–32, 41–56
2.3	7–40, 51–54, 59–80	7.5	7–22, 31–46, 51–56, 61–70
2.4	11–28, 39–54, 67–70	7.6	1–22, 39–45
2.5	11–50	7.7	7–12, 19–24, 29–36
3.1	9–36	7.8	9–76
3.2	7–50, 63–66	8.1	1–20, 29–54
3.3	15–22, 26–30, 35–36, 44–45	8.2	1–32
3.4	9–38	8.3	1–8, 15–27, 33–36
3.5	5–10, 13–18, 21	8.4	7–52
3.8	9–30	8.5	1–26
4.1	23–68, 73–74, 79–80	8.6	1–58
4.2	11–56, 93–96	8.7	1–41
4.3	9–36, 43–72	8.8	1–12, 23–40
4.4	11–56	9.1	9–58
4.5	7–22	9.2	7–33, 39–48
5.1	17–34, 37–50, 57–96	9.3	9–90
5.2	9–77		
5.3	9–62		
5.4	9–68		
5.5	11–54		
5.6	1–36		
5.7	7–48		
5.8	7–42		

NOTE: The back of your book has the answers to all odd homework problems. The student's solution manual demonstrates the method by which each odd answer is obtained.

SCHEDULE

Monday	Wednesday	Friday
Jan 22 Sections 1.1–1.2	Jan 24 Sections 1.3–1.5	Jan 26* Sections 1.6–1.7
Jan 29 Sections 2.1–2.2	Jan 31 Section 2.3	Feb 2* Sections 2.4–2.5
Feb 5 Sections 3.1–3.2	Feb 7 Section 3.3	Feb 9*[+] Section 3.4
Feb 12 Sections 3.5 and 3.8	Feb 14 Section 4.1	Feb 16* **EXAM 1**—Chapters 1, 2, 3
Feb 19 President's Day	Feb 21 Section 4.2	Feb 23*| Section 4.3
Feb 26 Section 4.4	Feb 28 Sections 5.1–5.2	Mar 2* Sections 5.3–5.5
Mar 5[#] Sections 5.6–5.7	Mar 7 Section 5.8	Mar 9* Sections 6.1–6.2
Mar 12 Section 6.3	Mar 14 **EXAM 2**—Chapters 4, 5	Mar 16* Section 6.4
Mar 19 Section 6.5	Mar 21 Section 7.1	Mar 23* Section 7.2
Mar 26 Spring Break	Mar 28 Spring Break	Mar 30 Spring Break
Apr 2 Sections 7.3–7.4	Apr 4 Section 7.5	Apr 6* Sections 7.6–7.7
Apr 9 Section 7.8	Apr 11 Section 8.1	Apr 13* Section 8.2
Apr 16 **EXAM 3**—Chapters 6, 7	Apr 18 Section 8.3	Apr 20* Sections 8.4-8.5
Apr 23 Sections 8.6–8.7	Apr 25 Section 8.8	Apr 27* Section 9.1
Apr 30 Section 9.2	May 2 Section 9.3	May 4* Review

Final Examinations May 7–11

* Weekly laboratory activity due by 5:00PM in the Mathematics Learning Center
[+] Last day to drop course via cyber bear
[#] Last day to drop course with drop/add form

ARAPAHOE COMMUNITY COLLEGE SYLLABUS

Revised Fall 2006

Course Number: MAT 106
Title: Survey of Algebra
Credits: 4

Instructor:
Phone:
E-mail:
Office Location (if applicable):
Office Hours (if applicable):

Important Dates
Last day to drop with refund (include date):
Last day to withdraw without refund (include date):

This course satisfies degree requirements for certain A.A.S. and A.G.S. degrees. It does not transfer to four year institutions, but serves as a prerequisite to transfer level courses MAT 121 College Algebra, MAT 123 Finite Mathematics, MAT 135/179 Introduction to Statistics/Lab, and MAT 155 Integrated Math I.

Catalog Description
Emphasizes problem solving with further study of equations, slope, inequalities, systems of equations, polynomials, quadratic equations, rational expressions, rational exponents, radical expressions, graphing and applications. A graphing calculator or equivalent software may be utilized.

Prerequisites
A student needs to have successfully completed (grade of C or better) MAT 090, Introductory Algebra, or achieved a CPT score of 61 to 84 in Elementary Algebra.

Corequisite:
MAT 111 Technology Lab for Algebra required.

Text
Bittinger, Ellenbogen, Johnson, *Intermediate Algebra: Graphs and Models* 2nd Ed., Addison Wesley, 2004. Supplemental Resources: Students may purchase the *Student Solutions Manual* from the Bookstore.

Required Course Material
Text and graph paper are required. If you plan to take College Algebra in the future, a TI-86 or comparable graphing calculator would be strongly recommended. If you plan to take Finite Mathematics or Introduction to Statistics in the future, a TI-83, TI-83+ or TI-84 graphing calculator would be strongly recommended.

Grading Criteria:

Makeup Policy:

Attendance Policy
Arapahoe Community College provides accommodations to qualified students with disabilities. To request accommodation, contact Disability Services in M2710.

The Math Department offers math support services (including tutoring, computer and calculator support, and other services) through the Mathematics Lab in room M3610. Please take advantage of this great opportunity to study with experienced tutors (generally faculty members) and your fellow classmates AND to obtain unlimited access to the math software we will be using in class!

Recommended Course Content: (Chapters and Topics in current Text.)

1. **Basics of Algebra and Graphing** (prerequisite material— for review)

1.1 Some Basics of Algebra
1.2 Operations with Real Numbers
1.3 Equivalent Algebraic Expressions
1.4 Exponential and Scientific Notation
1.5 Graphs
1.6 Mathematical Models and Problem Solving

2. **Functions, Linear Equations and Models**

2.1 Functions
2.2 Solving Linear Equations
2.3 Applications and Formulas
2.4 Linear Functions: Slope, Graphs, and Models
2.5 Another Look at Linear Graphs
2.6 Introduction to Curve Fitting: Point-Slope Form
2.7 Domains and the Algebra of Functions

3. **Systems of Equations and Problem Solving**

3.1 Systems of Equations in Two Variables
3.2 Solving by Substitution or Elimination
3.3 Solving Applications: Systems of Two Equations
3.4 Systems of Equations in Three Variables
3.5 Solving Applications: Systems of Three Equations

4. **Inequalities and Problem Solving**

4.1 Inequalities and Applications
4.2 Intersections, Unions and Compound Inequalities
4.3 Absolute-Value Equations and Inequalities
4.4 Inequalities in Two Variables

5. **Polynomials Functions**

5.1 Introduction to and Polynomials and Polynomial Functions
5.2 Multiplication of Polynomials
5.3 Polynomial Equations and Factoring
5.4 Equations Containing Trinomials of the Type $x^2 + bx + c$
5.5 Equations Containing Trinomials of the Type $ax^2 + bx + c, a \neq 1$
5.6 Equations Containing Perfect-Square Trinomials and Differences of Squares
5.7 Equations Containing Sums or Differences of Cubes
5.8 Applications of Polynomial Equations

6. **Rational Equations and Functions**

6.1 Rational Expressions and Functions: Multiplying and Dividing
6.2 Rational Expressions and Functions: Adding and Subtracting
6.3 Complex Rational Expressions
6.4 Rational Equations
6.5 Solving Applications Using Rational Equations
6.6 Division of Polynomials
6.7 Synthetic Division (optional)
6.8 Formulas, Applications, and Variation

TEACHING TIPS CORRELATED TO TEXTBOOK SECTIONS

Following is a listing of the objectives included in the Intermediate Algebra *text, as well as specific teaching tips provided by the contributing professors.*

1 Basics of Algebra and Graphing

SECTION TITLES AND OBJECTIVES

1.1 Some Basics of Algebra
Algebraic Expressions and Their Use ● Evaluating Algebraic Expressions ● Equations and Inequalities ● Sets of Numbers ● Introduction to the Graphing Calculator

1.2 Operations with Real Numbers
Absolute Value ● Order ● Addition, Subtraction, and Opposites ● Multiplication, Division, and Reciprocals

1.3 Equivalent Algebraic Expressions
The Commutative, Associative, and Distributive Laws ● Combining Like Terms ● Checking by Evaluating

1.4 Exponential and Scientific Notation
The Product and Quotient Rules ● The Zero Exponent ● Negative Integers as Exponents ● Simplifying $(a^m)^n$ ● Raising a Product or a Quotient to a Power ● Scientific Notation I Significant Digits and Rounding

1.5 Graphs
Points and Ordered Pairs ● Quadrants and Scale ● Graphs of Equations ● Nonlinear Equations

1.6 Solving Equations and Formulas
Equivalent Equations ● The Addition and Multiplication Principles ● Types of Equations ● Solving Formulas

1.7 Introduction to Problem Solving and Models
The Five-Step Strategy ● Translating to Algebraic Expressions ● Problem Solving ● Mathematical Models

TEACHING TIPS

General textbook tips:

- Explain to the students what the "Aha!" means in the exercise sets. Once my students know what to look for, they enjoy looking for the shortcuts.

- I like to assign the thinking and writing exercises ("TW"), the Interactive Discoveries, and the Collaborative Corners for group discussion. I find that students will not attempt the Interactive Discoveries when (and if!) they read the textbook. These are nice hands-on learning opportunities.

- Make use of the Teaching Tips located in the margin of the text. These can be really useful, especially when we forget how difficult this material can be to some students.

Karen Walters,
Arapahoe Community College

Section 1.1

Any course on the subject of algebra should probably begin by asking some fundamental questions: What is algebra? (The mathematical practice of letting variables, symbolized by letters, take the place of unknown numbers.) Where did it come from? (The middle east, an Arabic word.) Why is it important that I learn it? (Algebra is the universal language of science and is used in describing many natural phenomena. It is also a world unto itself that is still being explored by modern mathematicians.)

Matt B. Roscoe,
The University of Montana

◆ ◆ ◆

I find it easier for students to understand a Venn diagram when comparing sets of real numbers.

Karen Walters,
Arapahoe Community College

Sections 1.1 and 1.2

I spend a lot of time on order of operations. I explain to the students that their calculators follow the rules of order of operations, so they need to use parentheses very carefully. I often remind my students to put extra parentheses around the entire numerator and entire denominator of a fraction, as this is where they seem to make the most mistakes. I also need to remind them of the difference between the subtraction and negative sign keys on the calculator. This information is explained in the text, but I find that students need it to be reiterated.

Karen Walters,
Arapahoe Community College

Section 1.4

Show that while we have a definition for $(ab)^n$ we do not have a definition for $(a + b)^n$ or $(a - b)^n$. The course will later examine these patterns in the chapter on polynomials

Matt B. Roscoe,
The University of Montana

◆ ◆ ◆

Teach students how to read scientific notation from their calculators. I mark an answer as incorrect if they write the E in their answer. For example, they may write 3.87 E–6 instead of 3.87×10^{-6}. When students find roots of functions later on in the course, they will often get a value close to, but not equal to zero. I tell them that a general rule of thumb is to round to zero if the answer in scientific notation has an exponent less than or equal to -6.

Karen Walters,
Arapahoe Community College

Section 1.5

Point out that for univariate problems, the visual aid is the one dimensional number line. For bivariate problems, the visual aid is the two dimensional Cartesian plane. Seeing this pattern, students are often able to guess that dimensions (x-y-z) are required to visualize algebraic equations that have 3 variables.

Matt B. Roscoe,
The University of Montana

◆ ◆ ◆

I find that students often think of a graph as a picture reminiscent of a childhood connect-the-dots drawing. I think that it is worth spending the time in lecture to demonstrate that the line in a graph is actually an infinitely dense stream of individual solutions. A graph is continuous.

Matt B. Roscoe,
The University of Montana

Section 1.6.

Ask the students to think of an algebraic equation as a carefully balanced scale that must maintain equilibrium throughout the process of solving equations. If equilibrium is thrown off at any stage, then the final solution will be unbalanced (i.e., a false solution). Thus, tell students to mentally ask themselves if each algebraic step "maintains a balanced equation". I often demonstrate that forming equivalent expressions is the process that many teachers use to build equations that have certain answers, such as:

$$x = \frac{1}{2}$$

$$2x = 1$$

$$2x - 17 = 1 - 17$$

$$2x - 17 = -16$$

$$-3(2x - 17) = -3(-17)$$

$$-6x + 51 = 48$$

Matt B. Roscoe,
The University of Montana

Section 1.7

"INVALID DIM" is a common error that appears on the calculator when a plot is turned on. It helps to let the students know in advance that they should try turning off their plots when they get this error to avoid a lot of frustration.

Karen Walters,
Arapahoe Community College

2 Functions, Linear Equations, and Models

TEACHING TIPS

Assign many homework problems where they need to interpret graphs. In class, interpret linear regression graphs together. Discuss the pattern of the plotted points as a preview of future regressions such as higher order polynomial, exponential, or logarithmic regressions. Find examples of graphs that are relevant to the students. Look in newspapers or news magazines to find graphs that the class can interpret.

Karen Walters,
Arapahoe Community College

Section 2.1

Students have trouble with the definition of a function at first. It's a good idea to have several examples where one element of the domain is paired with more than one element of the range to emphasize that this does not represent a function and several examples where more than one element of the domain is paired with a single element of the range to emphasize that this can represent a function.

Kandace Kling,
Portland Community College

◆ ◆ ◆

Show students how to use the TABLE on their calculators. Have them set the independent variable to ASK so that they can enter their own *x*-values.

Karen Walters,
Arapahoe Community College

◆ ◆ ◆

"Your grade in this class is a function of ..."

"A farmer's yield is a function of ..."

"Your ... is a function of your level of education."

I like to start the discussion regarding functions with some "fill in the blanks" such as these and then ask students to create their own functions. I tell students that the science of modeling seeks to find a numerical relationship between the domain and the range of everyday functions like the ones that they have invented.

Matt B. Roscoe,
The University of Montana

◆ ◆ ◆

Function notation is tricky for many students. It is important to compare things like $f(a) + 2$ and $f(a + 2)$ for different functions (like $f(x) = 3x$). You should also use different function names like $g(x)$ and $k(t)$.

Kandace Kling,
Portland Community College

◆ ◆ ◆

Students need a lot of in class practice with the 2nd CALC menu and linear regression on their calculators. Set aside more time than you think you need for this as you will need to give the students a great deal of individual attention. Have students who have already mastered these techniques assist their classmates.

Karen Walters,
Arapahoe Community College

Section 2.1 and 2.2

Students need to make connections between formulas for functions, graphs of functions, and functions in numerical form. You should ask them to find $f(3)$ given a formula for $f(x)$, given a graph of $f(x)$, and given $f(x)$ in numerical form (for instance, a table of values.)

Kandace Kling,
Portland Community College

Section 2.2

My high school algebra teacher told us that to graph $y = mx + b$ we must first begin at b and move according to m. This approach seems to help students remember how to graph a linear equation.

Matt B. Roscoe,
The University of Montana

◆ ◆ ◆

A difficult problem for students is to find the value of t for which $m(t) = 4$. You should provide examples of this type using formulas, graphs, and tables.

Kandace Kling,
Portland Community College

◆ ◆ ◆

I think that it is worth foreshadowing the study of slope in calculus by pointing out that nonlinear graphs have a dynamic slope. Students often are very intuitive in deciding over which intervals a second degree polynomial equation has positive, negative and zero slopes.

Matt B. Roscoe,
The University of Montana

◆ ◆ ◆

Although finding an equation of a line should be a review for students at this level, they often have trouble when you ask them to find the formula for the linear function $f(x)$ such that $f(2) = -3$ and $f(-4) = 1$. You can also give this type of problem using a graph or a table of values. This is a good way to practice function notation.

Kandace Kling,
Portland Community College

Section 2.3

You can help your students visualize why perpendicular lines have negative reciprocal slopes using two overheads, each with an unlabeled Cartesian plane and the same line drawn in two different colors. Rotate one of the planes 90 degrees and then compare the slopes of the two lines. Use the same two overheads upside down for another example.

Matt B. Roscoe,
The University of Montana

Section 2.4

Curve fitting is an excellent opportunity to let students have some choice in their education. You will get over 51,000,000 hits on Google for a search for "linear data". I ask students to find some linear data that is of a personal interest for them to model. I ask them to pick two representative points to curve fit a model using the point slope equation and then compare their model with the least squares regression line.

Finally, I ask them to interpolate, extrapolate, and write a short report of their findings. Students often comment that this is a meaningful experience.

Matt B. Roscoe,
The University of Montana

Section 2.5

Students have difficulty with algebra of functions. I usually distribute the graphs of two functions on graph paper and have the students help me to determine by using points the sum, difference, product, and quotient of the two functions. This method is also useful for determining the domain of each of the operations.

Karen Walters,
Arapahoe Community College

3   Systems of Linear Equations and Problem Solving

SECTION TITLES AND OBJECTIVES

3.1   Systems of Equations in Two Variables
Translating ● Identifying Solutions ● Solving Systems Graphically ● Models

3.2   Solving by Substitution or Elimination
The Substitution Method ● The Elimination Method ● Comparing Methods

3.3   Solving Applications: Systems of Two Equations
Total-Value and Mixture Problems ● Motion Problems

3.4   Systems of Equations in Three Variables
Identifying Solutions ● Solving Systems in Three Variables ● Dependency, Inconsistency, and Geometric Considerations

3.5   Solving Applications: Systems of Three Equations
Applications of Three Equations in Three Unknowns

3.6   Elimination Using Matrices
Matrices and Systems ● Row-Equivalent Operations

3.7   Determinants and Cramer's Rule
Determinants of 2×2 Matrices ● Cramer's Rule: 2×2 Systems ● Cramer's Rule: 3×3 Systems

3.8   Business and Economics Applications
Break-Even Analysis ● Supply and Demand

TEACHING TIPS

Section 3.1

When teaching systems of linear equations in two variables, I usually pick a typical example of a system and solve it graphically, by substitution, and by elimination. I try to impress upon my students the beauty of mathematics that is displayed in such a demonstration. Each method follows a seemingly unrelated path to a single solution.

Matt B. Roscoe,
The University of Montana

◆ ◆ ◆

Emphasize the difference between a solution to a system of equations and a solution of an equation. Students often forget to go back and solve for the other variable(s) after solving for the first variable.

Kandace Kling,
Portland Community College

Section 3.2

I find that the use of colored markers (or chalk) is very helpful in solving systems of equations using substitution. Use a different color for each equation. The "substitution" is then easy to display, as the red equation solved for y replaces the y in the blue equation.

Matt B. Roscoe,
The University of Montana

Section 3.2 and 3.3

It is important to make a connection to the graphical solution when solving a system of two linear equations with two variables.

Kandace Kling,
Portland Community College

Section 3.3

It is important that students determine a reasonable solution to these problems before attempting them. They also should check the solutions in the original problems and determine whether their answers make sense. I tell students that word problems are the easiest type of problem because they will know when their answer is wrong if they have, for example, a solution with a negative time or physical measurement, or if the answer is outrageous, such as a car speed in the thousands or an age in the hundreds.

Karen Walters,
Arapahoe Community College

Section 3.4

I explain systems of equations in three unknowns by speaking of "generations of equations". Three parent equations in three unknowns are used to create two "2nd generation offspring" equations in two unknowns (using two sets of different parents) which are then used to create one final "3rd generation offspring" equation in one unknown. I even draw "family trees" of equations to exemplify the process.

Matt B. Roscoe,
The University of Montana

Sections 3.4 and 3.5

Solving systems of three equations can take a long time. I have my students solve only one system of three equations by hand on the test. I allow them to solve the application problems from section 3.5 using matrices on their calculators. They must set up the system of equations, give the corresponding augmented matrix, and state their answer either as an ordered triple or in a sentence answering the problem. Matrices are introduced in section 3.6, so you may want to work this section before assigning problems from section 3.5.

Karen Walters,
Arapahoe Community College

Section 3.5

I like to come back to the topic of solving a system of three linear equations with three variables when I get to the chapter on quadratics. Having students find quadratic models by setting up a system of three linear equations with three variables is a great way to review this topic while teaching them how to find a quadratic model.

Kandace Kling,
Portland Community College

Section 3.8

I ask the business students to help explain these problems to the class. Students seem to have an easier time with these problems than with the total-value, mixture, and motion problems, so I like to use this section as a confidence builder.

Karen Walters,
Arapahoe Community College

Cumulative Review of Chapters 1–3

This review makes a good group exercise. If you do not have time for all of the problems, assign particular problems to each group to present to the class.

Karen Walters,
Arapahoe Community College

4 Inequalities and Problem Solving

SECTION TITLES AND OBJECTIVES

4.1 Inequalities and Applications
Solutions of Inequalities ● Interval Notation and graphs ● The Addition Principle for Inequalities ● The Multiplication Principle for Inequalities ● Using the Principles Together ● Problem Solving

4.2 Solving Equations and Inequalities by Graphing
Solving Equations Graphically: The Intersect Method ● Solving Equations Graphically: The Zero Method ● Solving Inequalities Graphically ● Applications

4.3 Intersections, Unions, and Compound Inequalities
Intersections of Sets and Conjunctions of Sentences ● Unions of Sets and Disjunctions of Sentences ● Interval Notation and Domains

4.4 Absolute-Value Equations and Inequalities
Equations with Absolute Value ● Inequalities with Absolute Value

4.5 Inequalities in Two Variables
Graphs of Linear Inequalities ● Systems of Linear Inequalities

TEACHING TIPS

Section 4.1

Reversing the inequality symbol when one multiplies or divides both sides of an inequality by a negative often mystifies students. I try to show why this is true by having my students pick two random integers and place a correct inequality between the two numbers. Then I ask them to successively add, subtract, multiply, and divide both sides of the inequality by both positive and negative integers and reassign the correct inequality symbol for each result. I then ask my students to tell me when they need to switch the direction of the inequality.

Matt B. Roscoe,
The University of Montana

Section 4.2

Emphasize the difference between a solution to an inequality and a solution to an equation. Make sure they understand the broad range of solutions. I've had many students who thought that the only solutions to an inequality were the integers they wrote on the number line.

Kandace Kling,
Portland Community College

Section 4.3

I usually spend a fair amount of time on this section. To demonstrate compound inequalities, I like to use overhead transparencies. I put the individual inequalities on separate graphs in different colors, and then overlay them to show intersections and unions. For every problem, I have students write the solution using words ("and" or "or"), interval notation, set-builder notation, and a graph. This enables students with different learning styles to make connections between the representations and helps build a foundation for the study of absolute value inequalities.

Karen Walters,
Arapahoe Community College

◆ ◆ ◆

When teaching intersections, unions, and compound inequalities I usually make an overhead of three unlabeled horizontal number lines, each directly above the other, that I can project onto the white board. I then solve each inequality using two different colored markers. The graphs for each inequality are plotted using the two corresponding colors on the projected number lines. Finally, the intersection or union can easily be plotted on the third number line at the bottom.

Matt B. Roscoe,
The University of Montana

◆ ◆ ◆

Students have a difficult time writing compound inequalities. It's important to spend some time making sure they understand what they are representing when they write an inequality. One of the most common student errors that I see is writing nonsense inequalities like $3 > x > 5$.

Kandace Kling,
Portland Community College

Section 4.4

I like to teach absolute value problems by simply explaining to students that since the absolute value is defined as the distance from zero on the number line, the quantity inside the absolute value can either be positive or negative. Thus, if you desire to remove the absolute value from either an equation or an inequality you must consider two cases, one where the quantity inside the absolute value is positive and one where the quantity is negative.

For example:

$|x + 3| > 5$

$(x + 3) > 5$ or $-(x + 3) > 5$

Matt B. Roscoe,
The University of Montana

◆ ◆ ◆

Students like to remove the absolute value symbols before solving. Stress that they need to isolate the absolute value before removing the symbols. They should always check their answers.

Karen Walters,
Arapahoe Community College

◆ ◆ ◆

Students often have difficulties with absolute value inequalities. One thing I find helpful is to begin by solving an inequality like $|2x - 3| > 1$ using the graph of $f(x) = 2x - 3$. Then I have students check their algebraic solutions by looking at graphs.

Kandace Kling,
Portland Community College

Section 4.5

I distribute "coordinate cards" to the students when I teach inequalities in two variables. I give them a simple inequality and ask them to evaluate the inequality using their coordinate and then tell me if the inequality is true or false. I mark true coordinates on an overhead projected Cartesian plane in black and I mark false coordinates in red. The resulting graph leads to a discussion of how to determine the line of division between solutions and non-solutions as well as test points and shading.

Matt B. Roscoe,
The University of Montana

◆ ◆ ◆

I assign a project on linear programming at this point in the course. This introduces students to some applications of systems of linear inequalities and gives them a look at higher-level mathematics. For the project, I ask students to solve several linear programming problems. Then I have them create their own linear programming problem. Students enjoy applying their own creativity to this project.

Karen Walters,
Arapahoe Community College

5   Polynomials and Polynomials Functions

SECTION TITLES AND OBJECTIVES

5.1   Introduction to Polynomials and Polynomial Functions
Algebraic Expressions and Polynomials ● Polynomial Functions ● Adding Polynomials ● Opposites and Subtraction

5.2   Multiplication of Polynomials
Multiplying Monomials ● Multiplying Monomials and Binomials ● Multiplying Any Two Polynomials ● The Product of Two Binomials: FOIL ● Squares of Binomials ● Products of Sums and Differences ● Function Notation

5.3   Polynomial Equations and Factoring
Graphical Solutions ● The Principle of Zero Products ● Terms with Common Factors ● Factoring by Grouping ● Factoring and Equations

5.4   Equations Containing Trinomials of the Type $x^2 + bx + c$
Factoring Trinomials of the Type $x^2 + bx + c$ ● Equations Containing Trinomials ● Zeros and Factoring

5.5   Equations Containing Trinomials of the Type $ax^2 + bx + c$
Factoring Trinomials of the Type $ax^2 + bx + c$ ● Equations and Functions

5.6   Equations Containing Perfect-Square Trinomials and Differences of Squares
Perfect-Square Trinomials ● Differences of Squares ● More Factoring by Grouping ● Solving Equations

5.7   Equations Containing Sums or Differences of Cubes
Factoring Sums of Differences of Cubes ● Solving Equations

5.8   Applications of Polynomial Equations
Problem Solving ● Fitting Polynomial Functions to Data

TEACHING TIPS

Section 5.1

When teaching the language of polynomials, I give the students examples of polynomial expressions: a monomial, a binomial, a trinomial. Additionally, I give them examples of polynomials with different degrees and variables. I then create a table where we write each in descending order, identifying leading coefficients, terms, degrees, and names.

Matt B. Roscoe,
The University of Montana

Section 5.2

I find that the lattice method is a helpful tool for explaining the multiplication of polynomials. The lattice method is performed by creating a grid with the terms of one polynomial across the top of each column and the terms of the second polynomial at the start of each row. Each cell in the lattice is filled with the product of the terms of each row and column. Like terms appear along diagonals of the lattice. The lattice can also be used later to explain the idea of factoring.

Matt B. Roscoe,
The University of Montana

◆ ◆ ◆

I use Pascal's Triangle to show students how to find binomial expansions when binomials are raised to positive integer powers.

Karen Walters,
Arapahoe Community College

◆ ◆ ◆

Be sure to point out that we do have an exponent rule for products $(AB)^n$ but we do not have an exponent rule for sums $(A + B)^n$ or differences $(A - B)^n$. This is a common misconception.

Matt B. Roscoe,
The University of Montana

Section 5.3

I like to give the students a zero product property "pretest" when I teach about solving polynomial equations by factoring. I ask, what is two times zero. Then, what is zero times 5. And I continue on with five or six other zero multiplication facts. Finally I ask, "What can you tell me if I state that $AB = 0$?" Usually students will be able to state the zero product property.

Matt B. Roscoe,
The University of Montana

◆ ◆ ◆

I always do a problem such as $(x - 7)(x + 3) = 11$ when I teach the zero product property to point out that an "eleven product property" does not exist.

Matt B. Roscoe,
The University of Montana

Section 5.4

My students are more successful using the *ac*-method than guess and check as a means of factoring polynomials with a leading coefficient not equal to one.

Matt B. Roscoe,
The University of Montana

◆ ◆ ◆

I usually need to review factor trees at the beginning of this section. When students are using trial and error to find two factors with the desired sum, I instruct them to put the factors in a table in increasing order of the first factor.

Karen Walters,
Arapahoe Community College

Section 5.8

When solving application problems, I have the students write the answers in full sentences. Students are then usually able to catch incorrect answers and eliminate impossible solutions.

Karen Walters,
Arapahoe Community College

6 Rational Expressions, Equations, and Functions

SECTION TITLES AND OBJECTIVES

6.1 Rational Expressions and Functions: Multiplying and Dividing
Rational Functions ● Multiplying ● Simplifying Rational Expressions and Functions ● Dividing and Simplifying ● Vertical Asymptotes

6.2 Rational Expressions and Functions: Adding and Subtracting
When Denominators Are the Same ● When Denominators Are Different

6.3 Complex Rational Expressions
Multiplying by 1 ● Dividing Two Rational Expressions

6.4 Rational Equations
Solving Rational Equations

6.5 Solving Applications Using Rational Equations
Problems Involving Work ● Problems Involving Motion

6.6 Division of Polynomials
Dividing by a Monomial ● Dividing by a Polynomial

6.7 Synthetic Division
Streamlining Long Division ● The Remainder Theorem

6.8 Formulas, Applications, and Variation
Formulas ● Direct Variation ● Inverse Variation ● Joint and Combined Variation ● Models

TEACHING TIPS

I begin the chapter by stressing the Student Notes. The procedures covered in this chapter are by their nature rather long. Stress to the students the importance of showing their work, especially with rational expressions. Tell them not to squeeze the problems together because it can become very confusing quickly. This is a difficult chapter. Generally, I have the lowest exam scores on this chapter.

Tamie D. McCabe,
Redlands Community College

Section 6.1

I spend some extra time on the graphs of rational functions. We compare intercepts with holes in the graph and discuss the limitations of graphing calculators for these features.

Karen Walters,
Arapahoe Community College

◆ ◆ ◆

With rational expressions and fractions, some students like to use the notation "/" to represent division. Make sure that students see that something like $x + 1/x - 4$ is not the same as $(x + 1)/(x + 4)$. I always encourage the use of the horizontal division bar!

Terry Reeves,
Red Rocks Community College

◆ ◆ ◆

I find that one of the biggest challenges to teaching rational expressions, equations, and functions is the fact that many of my developmental mathematics students still struggle with fractions. I always begin this chapter with a review of fraction arithmetic.

Matt B. Roscoe,
The University of Montana

◆ ◆ ◆

If students want to simplify something like $\dfrac{x+2}{x-3}$ by crossing out the x's $\left(\text{which would then} = -\dfrac{2}{3},\right)$ show them that this isn't true by substituting a value such as $x = 1$. This would prove that $\dfrac{x+2}{x-3}$ isn't equivalent to $-\dfrac{2}{3}$ since it doesn't work for all real values that would make the original expression defined.

Terry Reeves,
Red Rocks Community College

◆ ◆ ◆

Students tend to multiply entire numerators and entire denominators before simplifying, only to find that they have difficulty simplifying. I stress to them that they always want to simplify before doing any multiplication. I have them work some larger problems both ways to illustrate that simplifying first is the easier and more efficient method.

Karen Walters,
Arapahoe Community College

Section 6.1 and 6.2

I also remind students (almost daily) that when simplifying by canceling, you can only cancel factors and not terms. Students seem to want to cancel the terms in a rational expression instead of taking the time to factor the polynomial and correctly cancel the factors.

Tamie D. McCabe,
Redlands Community College

Section 6.2

Inspiration for the operations with rational expressions can be drawn from fraction arithmetic. Before demonstrating how to multiply two rational expressions I usually multiply two fractions. I continue this format for division, addition, and subtraction.

Matt B. Roscoe,
The University of Montana

Section 6.3

This is a great place to practice function notation. Have students find the difference quotient $\dfrac{f(x+h)-f(x)}{h}$ for a rational function after covering complex rational expressions. Compare $f(a) + 2$ and $f(a + 2)$ for rational functions.

Kandace Kling,
Portland Community College

Section 6.4

Stress the difference between simplifying an expression and solving an equation. This is the chapter where a lot of students confuse the techniques. Students will try to clear an expression of fractions after they learn how to clear an equation of fractions. It is important to make sure that students have it clear in their minds whether they are simplifying an expression or solving an equation, and which techniques apply depending on the situation.

Kandace Kling,
Portland Community College

◆ ◆ ◆

Rational equations can be solved by multiplying both sides of an equation by the LCD, but other methods also exist. When a proportion exists, one can cross multiply. Alternatively, one can create common denominators and then set numerators equal. I think that it is worth noting that there are multiple paths to the same answer when solving rational equations.

Matt B. Roscoe,
The University of Montana

◆ ◆ ◆

This is a great place to emphasize the domain of a function. When solving rational equations, I have students begin by writing down any values that need to be excluded from the domain (due to division by zero.) This is also a good place to begin talking about the dangers of dividing both sides of an equation by an expression that contains a variable.

Kandace Kling,
Portland Community College

Section 6.5

Problems involving work are classic algebra problems which are often quite vexing for students. Take extra time to familiarize students with these problems. Point out that summing or averaging the work time for the two is an incorrect approach. Additionally, show that the time to complete a task together should fall somewhere between the time it takes each to complete half the work.

Matt B. Roscoe,
The University of Montana

◆ ◆ ◆

To solve application problems, it is helpful for students to set up a table for the information. This helps keep the information and the students organized.

Tamie D. McCabe,
Redlands Community College

Section 6.6

I begin this section by having the students work some long division problems with numbers to refresh their memories and to build their confidence with problems they already know how to solve. I then present a polynomial long division problem alongside a simple long division problem to show them the parallel steps involved.

Karen Walters,
Arapahoe Community College

◆ ◆ ◆

Synthetic division looks easy and involves a lot less writing than the traditional polynomial long division. However, point out that this method only works with linear divisors. Students can miss this small but important detail.

Terry Reeves
Red Rocks Community College

Section 6.8

I often use the ideal gas law $PV = nRT$ to discuss direct and inverse variation. I usually solve for pressure and discuss the effects of temperature and volume on a fixed quantity of gas. Most students have some familiarity with this physical phenomenon.

Matt B. Roscoe,
The University of Montana

◆ ◆ ◆

When discussing variation, we talk about driving. Direct variation: If one increases the pressure on the gas (I let the students tell me the outcome) the speed increases. Both are increasing; therefore, this is a direct variation.

Inverse variation: If one increases the pressure on the brake pedal then the speed decreases (again I let the student tell me the outcome). One is increasing while the other one is decreasing; therefore, this is inverse variation. If one increases the pressure on the gas then the speed increases and then what may happen? Try to have the students think of another outcome that would increase. Some responses have included: increase the chances of a getting a speeding ticket and increase the chance of getting in an accident.

Tamie D. McCabe,
Redlands Community College

7 Exponents and Radical Functions

SECTION TITLES AND OBJECTIVES

7.1 Radical Expressions, Functions, and Models
Square Roots and Square Root Functions ● Expressions of the Form $\sqrt{a^2}$ ● Cube Roots ● Odd and Even nth Roots ● Radical Functions and Models

7.2 Rational Numbers as Exponents
Rational Exponents ● Negative Rational Exponents ● Laws of Exponents ● Simplifying Radical Expressions

7.3 Multiplying Radical Expressions
Multiplying Radical Expressions ● Simplifying by Factoring ● Multiplying and Simplifying

7.4 Dividing Radical Expressions
Dividing and Simplifying ● Rationalizing Denominators and Numerators (Part 1)

7.5 Expressions Containing Several Radical Terms
Adding and Subtracting Radical Expressions ● Products and Quotients of Two or More Radical Terms ● Rationalizing Denominators and Numerators (Part 2) ● Terms with Differing Indices

7.6 Solving Radical Equations
The Principle of Powers ● Equations with Two Radical Terms

7.7 Geometric Applications
Using the Pythagorean Theorem ● Two Special Triangles

7.8 The Complex Numbers
Imaginary and Complex Numbers ● Addition and Subtraction ● Multiplication ● Conjugates and Division ● Powers of i

TEACHING TIPS

I begin this chapter by asking the students how to undo an addition problem and a multiplication problem. Then I tell them that in this chapter we will undo an exponent. If something is squared then we will take the square root; if it is cubed then we'll take the cube root; and so on.

Tamie D. McCabe,
Redlands Community College

Section 7.1

Students get confused with the simplification of $\sqrt{x^2} = |x|$ instead of $\sqrt{x^2} = x$. It is useful to have a discussion regarding whether x is a negative number, positive number, or zero. Instead of seeing x as being a variable which can represent any real number, students tend to see x as positive and $-x$ as negative.

Terry Reeves,
Red Rocks Community College

◆ ◆ ◆

Stress that students can test their theories with numbers. Students often think that they can simplify something like $\sqrt{2x + 3}$ to $\sqrt{2x} + \sqrt{3}$. If they compare $\sqrt{9 + 16}$ to $\sqrt{9}$ plus $\sqrt{16}$, they very quickly see that their simplification is incorrect.

Kandace Kling,
Portland Community College

◆ ◆ ◆

When simplifying, I use a sale. For instance, if we have $\sqrt{n^3}$ then it is a two for one sale. We show the one that we pay for and the extra goes back on the rack (inside the radical). $\sqrt[4]{n^6}$, then it is a four for one sale; we show the one we pay for and have two extra that go back on the rack.

Tamie D. McCabe,
Redlands Community College

Section 7.2

Radical exponents are very important. Students in subsequent math classes often struggle with this topic. Make sure you spend sufficient time on this topic and work with several problems converting between radical form and rational exponent form.

Kandace Kling,
Portland Community College

◆ ◆ ◆

Before diving into the subject of rational exponents, I remind my students that our discussion regarding exponents has proceeded from the naturals to the integers. I ask them what would be the next logical area of study with respect to exponents. Students usually respond "exponents that are decimals." I then indicate that a decimal is a convenient method for writing fractions, and thus rational exponents.

Matt B. Roscoe,
The University of Montana

◆ ◆ ◆

One of the problems that even calculus students struggle with has to do with rational exponents. It might seem a little weird, but students do need to see and do many problems with constant bases. Students often forget the order of operations when they are working a problem with exponents. For instance, they will try to multiply 2 and 3 when they encounter something like $2 \cdot 3^{\frac{4}{5}}$ or they will simplify

$$\frac{3^{\frac{1}{2}}}{3^{\frac{2}{3}}} = 1^{\frac{1}{2}-\frac{2}{3}}$$

Kandace Kling,
Portland Community College

Section 7.3

In the exercise sets, there are some nice true/false questions (for example, see section 7.3, problems 1–6). I think these types of questions are excellent for students, but they should also be able to also justify their answers. Many students will answer that a statement is true and justify it by showing that it is true for a specific number. This leads to a good discussion that an answer is false if one counterexample is found, so to answer true, the statement must be true for ALL possible cases.

Terry Reeves,
Red Rocks Community College

◆ ◆ ◆

Since a radical is equivalent to an exponent, it makes sense that again we find that we have a rule for $(AB)^2 = A^2B^2$, but no such rule exists for $(A + B)^2$ or $(A - B)^2$.

Matt B. Roscoe,
The University of Montana

Section 7.4

I impress upon my students that the process of simplifying radical expressions is necessary so that we can communicate unambiguously. Just like with fractions where multiple representations of the same number exist

$$\left(\frac{9}{6} = \frac{3}{2} = \frac{75}{50}\right),$$

we find the same thing with radicals $\sqrt{72} = 3\sqrt{8} = 6\sqrt{2}$. This process of simplifying radical expressions also allows us to identify like radical expressions that can be combined using addition.

Matt B. Roscoe,
The University of Montana

Section 7.5

When simplifying expressions with radical terms, some students might see this more easily if a substitution is used. For example, for something like $4\sqrt{7} + 2\sqrt{7}$, let $u = \sqrt{7}$. The expression now becomes $4u + 2u$, which equals $6u$. Then, back substitute to finish the problem.

Terry Reeves,
Red Rocks Community College

Section 7.8

I often begin our study of the complex numbers with an equation such as $x^2 - 4x + 5 = 0$ and explain to my students that the solution to such an equation was an open ended question up until the sixteenth century. I then promise them that at the end of the class we will be able to show that the equation indeed does have a solution and that the solution requires a whole new kind of number. I leave the equation, "the hook", on the board and present the operations of the complex numbers. At the end of the period I come back to the hook and tell my students that one solution is $2 + i$ and have them verify the solution.

Matt B. Roscoe,
The University of Montana

◆　◆　◆

When working with the powers of i, I show the powers to i^8 and let the students see the pattern and ask them to give a possible rule. I find the students understand this concept better using i^4 instead of i^2.

Tamie D. McCabe,
Redlands Community College

8 Quadratic Functions and Equations

SECTION TITLES AND OBJECTIVES

8.1 Quadratic Equations
The Principle of Square Roots • Completing the Square • Problem Solving

8.2 The Quadratic Formula
Solving Using the Quadratic Formula • Approximating Solutions

8.3 Applications Involving Quadratic Equations
Solving Problems • Solving Formulas

8.4 Studying Solutions of Quadratic Equations
The Discriminant • Writing Equations from Solutions

8.5 Equations Reducible to Quadratic
Recognizing Equations in Quadratic Form • Radical and Rational Equations

8.6 Quadratic Functions and Their Graphs
The Graph of $f(x) = ax^2$ • The Graph of $f(x) = a(x - h)^2$ • The Graph of $f(x) = a(x - h)^2 + k$

8.7 More About Graphing Quadratic Functions
Finding the Vertex • Finding Intercepts

8.8 Problem Solving and Quadratic Functions
Maximum and Minimum Problems • Fitting Quadratic Functions to Data

8.9 Polynomial and Rational Inequalities
Quadratic and Other Polynomial Inequalities • Rational Inequalities

TEACHING TIPS

At the beginning of this chapter, remind students that graphs of quadratic functions are always parabolic. If they are using a graphing calculator, they should realize that unless they see a parabola, they don't have a complete graph.

Terry Reeves,
Red Rocks Community College

◆ ◆ ◆

I like to begin this chapter by doing a quick review of factoring. Then, when given a perfect square trinomial. we begin with the principle of square roots.

Tamie D. McCabe,
Redlands Community College

Section 8.1

After looking at the various techniques for solving quadratic equations, I spend some time with my students discussing the different techniques and when they work well. I like to follow this up by having them solve several different types of quadratic equations, and I also include a few linear equations.

Kandace Kling,
Portland Community College

◆ ◆ ◆

I use PowerPoint slides to show the steps needed to complete the square. While the steps are on the screen, I do several examples and allow the students do a few on their own.

Tamie D. McCabe,
Redlands Community College

Section 8.1 or 8.4

Ask the students to think about whether or not all parabolas have y-intercepts. Why or why not?

Terry Reeves,
Red Rocks Community College

Sections 8.1 and 8.2

Tell the students that the highest exponent will give them the possible number of solutions. Remind them that the $\pm$ is two solutions, not one. Students will often forget to work out the problem. For example, they will leave their answer as $x = 4 \pm 6$ instead of $x = -2$ and $x = 10$.

Tamie D. McCabe,
Redlands Community College

Section 8.2

The derivation of the quadratic formula is a powerful demonstration of the usefulness of algebra to generalize a process, namely completing the square. I usually give a numerical example of completing the square with a quadratic with a leading coefficient not equal to 1, such as $3x^2 + 7x - 2 = 0$ and then next to the numerical example I ask students to help me repeat the process in general for $ax^2 + bx + c = 0$. Finally, I use the quadratic formula to re-solve the original problem to show that it indeed yields the same solution.

Matt B. Roscoe,
The University of Montana

◆ ◆ ◆

Stress the order of operations when doing the quadratic formula. It is amazing how quickly students forget it.

Often when working with equations that are reducible to quadratic, students do not finish the problem. They will forget to solve for the original variable when we have let $u = a$ variable or an expression.

Tamie D. McCabe,
Redlands Community College

Section 8.4

I like to test student knowledge of the discriminant by asking them to match three discriminant values to three graphs of $y = ax^2 + bx + c$; one with two x-intercepts, one with one x-intercept and one with no x-intercepts.

Matt B. Roscoe,
The University of Montana

Section 8.6

Although my students have studied quadratic equations and their graphs in beginning algebra, I find that I have to spend much time in this chapter reviewing the techniques for graphing a quadratic function by hand.

Kandace Kling,
Portland Community College

◆ ◆ ◆

I like to come back to the topic of solving a system of three linear equations with three variables in this chapter. Having students find quadratic models by setting up a system of three linear equations with three variables is a great way to review this topic while teaching them how to find a quadratic model.

Kandace Kling,
Portland Community College

Section 8.7

Really emphasize that before completing the square, the leading coefficient must be one. In Example 2 in the text, this process is shown. Teach this carefully because examples like this can be confusing to students.

Terry Reeves,
Red Rocks Community College

◆ ◆ ◆

When finding the vertex of a parabola I point out that the x-intercepts can be found where $f(x) = 0$ or where $ax^2 + bx + c = 0$. The quadratic formula provides these two locations. I then ask how we can find the x coordinate for the vertex. Looking at the graph it becomes apparent that the x coordinate for the vertex is found in the middle of the two x-intercepts or the average of the two solutions that the quadratic formula presents, namely

$$\frac{-b}{2a}.$$

Indicate that this also is true for a quadratic that has no x-intercepts.

Matt B. Roscoe,
The University of Montana

Section 8.8

Quadratic modeling is a great opportunity to unify many topics that the course presents: linear equations, systems of linear equations, quadratic equations, and graphing quadratic equations. I usually create an extra credit opportunity and ask the students to model federal Medicare expenditures using a quadratic function, and write a short report on the future of the program. I enjoy grading the results.

Matt B. Roscoe,
The University of Montana

9 Exponential and Logarithmic Functions

SECTION TITLES AND OBJECTIVES

9.1 Composite and Inverse Functions
Composite Functions ● Inverses and One-to-One Functions ● Finding Formulas for Inverses ● Graphing Functions and Their Inverses ● Inverse Functions and Composition

9.2 Exponential Functions
Graphing Exponential Functions ● Equations with x and y Interchanged ● Applications of Exponential Functions

9.3 Logarithmic Functions
Graphs of Logarithmic Functions ● Common Logarithms ● Equivalent Equations ● Solving Certain Logarithmic Equations

9.4 Properties of Logarithmic Functions
Logarithms of Products ● Logarithms of Powers ● Logarithms of Quotients ● Using the Properties Together

9.5 Natural Logarithms and Changing Bases
The Base e and Natural Logarithms ● Changing Logarithmic Bases ● Graphs of Exponential and Logarithmic Functions, Base e

9.6 Solving Exponential and Logarithmic Equations
Solving Exponential Equations ● Solving Logarithmic Equations

9.7 Applications of Exponential and Logarithmic Functions
Applications of Logarithmic Functions ● Applications of Exponential Functions

TEACHING TIPS

Section 9.1

Students seem to struggle at first with the composition of functions. Textbooks read $f \circ g$ in at least three ways. It is best to choose one of them and not mention the others. Additionally, I don't use technology with this topic because it usually confuses the students further.

Tamie D. McCabe,
Redlands Community College

Section 9.2

I employ a confetti approach to introduce the exponential function $y = 2^x$. I find a large piece of newspaper and claim that I initially have one piece of paper (0, 1). Tearing it in half, I now have two pieces (1, 2). Placing both pieces of paper on top of each other and tearing again, I now have 4 pieces (2, 4) ... (3, 8), (4, 16), (5, 32), (6, 64) ... Then I ask my student how they would predict how many pieces I had if I had torn the paper n times. The generalized definition follows. Repeat the experiment, keeping track of the size of the sheet of paper (0, 1), (1, 1/2), (2, 1/4), (3, 1/8) ... for another example of

$$y = \left(\frac{1}{2}\right)^x.$$

Matt B. Roscoe,
The University of Montana

◆ ◆ ◆

Compound interest is an important topic that all students will be faced with in the real world of credit card debt, home mortgages, and car loans. Spend time on this subject. Your instruction may have a profound effect on the future decisions that your students make. I usually compare the results of investing in two competing savings accounts, one with a high number of compounding periods and low interest rate, another with a lower number of compounding periods and a higher interest rate.

Matt B. Roscoe,
The University of Montana

Section 9.2 and 9.3

Translations of graphs are more understandable to the students if I first do several shifts on the board in several colors. When they first see it on a graphing calculator the black lines seem to turn into one line. After graphing a few on the board, the students can find the difference on the graphing calculator much more easily.

Tamie D. McCabe,
Redlands Community College

Section 9.4

The Power Rule for Logarithms can be easily misread. The property states that $\log_a M^P = P\log_a M$. Students often misinterpret that $(\log_a M)^P$ is also equal to $P\log_a M$, which is incorrect.

Terry Reeves,
Red Rocks Community College

◆ ◆ ◆

I find that students are often mystified by the sudden appearance of the number e in the exponential function, which is often given little or no explanation at the intermediate algebra level. As math instructors we know that e^x is important due to the fact that it is the only function that is its own derivative. You can express this to students at this level by noting that $y = e^x$ has a slope that is equal to the value of the function. Additionally, in application form, it is the appropriate base we use in situations of continuous compounding savings accounts.

Matt B. Roscoe,
The University of Montana

◆ ◆ ◆

The product and quotient rules for logs can also be easily misread. I've often seen students incorrectly write these rules. This is noted in the caution box in section 9.4; make extra note of this to the students.

Terry Reeves,
Red Rocks Community College

Section 9.6

When solving exponential and logarithmic equations, I show the students that there are several ways to solve the problems. They need to recognize what type of problem they are working with before trying to solve it.

Tamie D. McCabe,
Redlands Community College

◆ ◆ ◆

When working with log functions, I've often seen the mistake where students will treat "log" as a stand alone value. For example, when solving something like $\log(x) = 2$, I've often seen the result given as

$$x = \frac{2}{\log}.$$

Or, when calculating the value of

$$x = \frac{\log 3}{\log 4},$$

the answer is incorrectly given as

$$x = \frac{3}{4}.$$

Terry Reeves,
Red Rocks Community College

Section 9.7

Students seem to grasp the applications of exponential and logarithmic problems much more quickly then any other type.

Tamie D. McCabe,
Redlands Community College

Conic Sections

SECTION TITLES AND OBJECTIVES

10.1 Conic Sections: Parabolas and Circles
Parabolas • The Distance and Midpoint Formulas • Circles
10.2 Conic Sections: Ellipses
Ellipses Centered at $(0, 0)$ • Ellipses Centered at (h, k)
10.3 Conic Sections: Hyperbolas
Hyperbolas • Hyperbolas (Nonstandard Form) • Classifying Graphs of Equations
10.4 Nonlinear Systems of Equations
Systems Involving One Nonlinear Equation • Systems of Two Nonlinear Equations • Problem Solving

TEACHING TIPS

I begin this chapter by reviewing the graphs of quadratic equations with the students.

Tamie D. McCabe,
Redlands Community College

Section 10.1

When students transform a parabolic equation to standard form, have them check their work by expanding their standard form back to $y = ax^2 + bx + c$ or $x = ay^2 + by + c$. When first introducing this idea, it is a good check to do.

I strongly suggest doing the derivation of the distance formula in 10.1. It is presented in the section, but often students won't read it, or they don't understand what's being presented without some outside help. At first glance, the formula seems complicated, but the motivation behind it will help some students to retain it better than they would if they tried to memorize it without any basis for understanding.

The midpoint formula is often confused with the distance formula. Show why the midpoint formula adds the x and y values. Again, give context to the formula so that it makes sense.

Terry Reeves,
Red Rocks Community College

◆ ◆ ◆

I try to give my students charts of the sections so they have the information at hand.

Tamie D. McCabe,
Redlands Community College

Section 10.1 and 10.2

I have found it helpful to discuss the circles with the ellipses sections.

Tamie D. McCabe,
Redlands Community College

Section 10.2

If you have a document camera projector in the classroom, use it to demonstrate the creation of an ellipse with stick pins and string on a piece of corrugated cardboard. Do several examples with different string lengths and foci placements. This sort of demonstration leads intuitively to the derivation of the equation of an ellipse.

Matt B. Roscoe,
The University of Montana

◆ ◆ ◆

Drawing an ellipse helps the students understand this concept. Find a piece of string (the length of this string is the constant referred to in the definition). Then take two thumbtacks (the foci) and stick them on a piece of cardboard so that the distance between them is less than the length of the string. Now attach the ends of the string to the thumbtacks and using the point of a pencil, pull the string taut. Keeping the string taut, rotate the pencil around the two thumbtacks. The pencil traces out an ellipse.

Tamie D. McCabe,
Redlands Community College

◆ ◆ ◆

To produce ellipses on a whiteboard, visit a hardware store and buy several suction cup hangers that are typically sold for use in the kitchen or bath. These can be stuck to the white board and a string can be strung between the two hangers to create ellipses of various sizes and shapes. Again, this sort of demonstration leads intuitively to the derivation of the equation of an ellipse.

Matt B. Roscoe,
The University of Montana

Section 10.3

Tell the students that the asymptotes of a hyperbola are not part of the hyperbola, but they do serve as a guide for graphing a hyperbola.

I also remind students that when working with a circle and their graphing calculator they need to square the screen so that the circle looks correct. I do not use the conics application on the graphing calculator. I believe the students do not get the best understanding of conics from the graphing calculator.

Tamie D. McCabe,
Redlands Community College

◆ ◆ ◆

Remind the students that the nonstandard hyperbola was visited in chapter 6.8 in the study of inverse variation.

Matt B. Roscoe,
The University of Montana

11   Sequences, Series, and the Binomial Theorem

SECTION TITLES AND OBJECTIVES

11.1   Sequences and Series
Sequences ● Finding the General Term ● Sums and Series ● Sigma Notation ● Graphs of Sequences
11.2   Arithmetic Sequences and Series
Arithmetic Sequences ● Sum of the First n Terms of an Arithmetic Sequence ● Problem Solving
11.3   Geometric Sequences and Series
Geometric Sequences ● Sum of the First n Terms of a Geometric Sequence ● Infinite Geometric Series ● Problem Solving
11.4   The Binomial Theorem
Binomial Expansion Using Pascal's Triangle ● Binomial Expansion Using Factorial Notation

TEACHING TIPS

I tell the students about Karl Friedrich Gauss and the story of how he recognized patterns. Also, I stress the terminology in this chapter. I develop short quizzes with concepts similar to those at the end of the sections.

Tamie D. McCabe,
Redlands Community College

Section 11.1

When introducing sequences, carefully show the notation first. Most students are not familiar with the "a_n" notation; the subscript may merit some extra explanation. As the chapter continues, students tend to use the terms "series" and "sequences" interchangeably. Caution them about this, and make sure they know the difference between the two.

Terry Reeves,
Red Rocks Community College

Section 11.2

Often students think of arithmetic sequences as a linear sort of phenomenon that can be modeled by $y = mx + b$. Point out the difference between discrete and continuous phenomena in nature (number of trees in the forest and the size of each tree) and the importance of a language for each type of phenomenon.

Matt B. Roscoe,
The University of Montana

Section 11.3

For the sum of a geometric series

$$S = \frac{a}{1 - r},$$

this can be tricky when the ratio r is negative. Emphasize this point.

Terry Reeves,
Red Rocks Community College

◆ ◆ ◆

Again, students often think of geometric sequences as exponential phenomena that can be modeled by $y = ab^n$. It is important to show the difference between the discrete and continuous requirements on the variable n in the model.

Matt B. Roscoe,
The University of Montana

Section 11.4

Since many students in my class will eventually enroll in a statistics and probability course, I usually take the time to show them that Pascal's Triangle is related to combinations - $C(n, k)$.

Matt B. Roscoe,
The University of Montana

◆ ◆ ◆

I try to bring in statistics when discussing the binomial theorem. Students tend to grasp the idea when they can relate to where they may see it again.

Tamie D. McCabe,
Redlands Community College

Extra Practice Exercises

EXTRA PRACTICE 1
Addition And Subtraction Of Real Numbers
Use after Section 1.2 Name_____

Examples: Add.

a) $5+9=14$

$-5+9=4$

b) $5+(-9)=-4$

$-5+(-9)=-14$

c) $-\dfrac{5}{8}+\dfrac{2}{3}=-\dfrac{15}{24}+\dfrac{16}{24}=\dfrac{1}{24}$

$6.7+(-8.1)=-1.4$

Add.

1. $-4+(-5)=$ _____
2. $-7+6=$ _____
3. $8+(-3)=$ _____
4. $-8+8=$ _____
5. $-11+(-17)=$ _____
6. $-15+3=$ _____
7. $-6+15=$ _____
8. $5+(-7)=$ _____
9. $18+(-3)=$ _____
10. $-9+(-19)=$ _____
11. $-9+2=$ _____
12. $6+(-7)=$ _____
13. $-3+(-1)=$ _____
14. $-4+(-4)=$ _____
15. $18+(-15)=$ _____
16. $-15+4=$ _____
17. $-7+19=$ _____
18. $16+(-9)=$ _____
19. $24+(-11)=$ _____
20. $-5+6=$ _____
21. $-3+(-9)=$ _____
22. $12+(-7)=$ _____
23. $-7+14=$ _____
24. $-2+(-5)=$ _____
25. $-21+21=$ _____
26. $-8+2=$ _____
27. $9+(-11)=$ _____
28. $-5+(-11)=$ _____
29. $-\dfrac{3}{4}+\left(-\dfrac{2}{5}\right)=$ _____
30. $\dfrac{7}{8}+\left(-\dfrac{3}{4}\right)=$ _____
31. $-\dfrac{5}{12}+\dfrac{2}{3}=$ _____
32. $-\dfrac{1}{5}+\left(-\dfrac{1}{3}\right)=$ _____
33. $\dfrac{7}{9}+\left(-\dfrac{1}{4}\right)=$ _____
34. $-\dfrac{1}{2}+\dfrac{5}{7}=$ _____
35. $-9.5+4.3=$ _____
36. $-8.7+15.2=$ _____
37. $-3.1+(-6.8)=$ _____
38. $15.6+(-19.2)=$ _____
39. $-7.5+9.1=$ _____
40. $-6.5+(-9.9)=$ _____

EXTRA PRACTICE 1 (continued)
Addition And Subtraction Of Real Numbers
Use after Section 1.2   Name_____

Examples: Subtract.

$6 - 9 = 6 + (-9) = -3$ $-\dfrac{2}{3} - \dfrac{4}{5} = -\dfrac{10}{15} + \left(-\dfrac{12}{15}\right) = -\dfrac{22}{15}$

$-6 - 9 = -6 + (-9) = -15$ $6.9 - (-5.2) = 6.9 + 5.2 = 12.1$
$6 - (-9) = 6 + 9 = 15$
$-6 - (-9) = -6 + 9 = 3$

Subtract.

41. $-6 - 10 =$ _____   42. $-7 - (-7) =$ _____

43. $15 - (-3) =$ _____   44. $6 - 11 =$ _____

45. $-9 - 12 =$ _____   46. $-8 - (-15) =$ _____

47. $3 - 8 =$ _____   48. $-7 - 3 =$ _____

49. $-5 - (-6) =$ _____   50. $1 - (-13) =$ _____

51. $-7 - (-4) =$ _____   52. $-8 - 2 =$ _____

53. $9 - (-2) =$ _____   54. $-19 - (-6) =$ _____

55. $7 - 16 =$ _____   56. $15 - 3 =$ _____

57. $-15 - 4 =$ _____   58. $5 - (-8) =$ _____

59. $-9 - (-7) =$ _____   60. $6 - 11 =$ _____

61. $5 - (-6) =$ _____   62. $-15 - (-7) =$ _____

63. $3 - 15 =$ _____   64. $6 - (-8) =$ _____

65. $-2 - 6 =$ _____   66. $17 - 21 =$ _____

67. $19 - (-4) =$ _____   68. $-6 - (-12) =$ _____

69. $\dfrac{5}{8} - \dfrac{1}{2} =$ _____   70. $-\dfrac{3}{4} - \dfrac{2}{3} =$ _____

71. $-\dfrac{9}{10} - \left(-\dfrac{3}{4}\right) =$ _____   72. $-\dfrac{1}{5} - \dfrac{1}{6} =$ _____

73. $\dfrac{7}{12} - \left(-\dfrac{2}{5}\right) =$ _____   74. $-\dfrac{5}{9} - \left(-\dfrac{5}{6}\right) =$ _____

75. $7.8 - (-13.2) =$ _____   76. $-4.1 - 16.3 =$ _____

77. $8.7 - 12.4 =$ _____   78. $-8.2 - (-5.5) =$ _____

79. $-5.3 - 1.8 =$ _____   80. $6.9 - (-3.4) =$ _____

EXTRA PRACTICE 2
Solving Linear Equations Using the Addition and Multiplication Principles
Use after Section 1.6   **Name**_____
_____

Solve.

1. $x + 37 = 98$ _____   2. $y - 53 = 141$ _____   3. $59 + a = -123$ _____

4. $-72 + t = -40$ _____   5. $-55 = x + 32$ _____   6. $a + \dfrac{5}{6} = -\dfrac{1}{2}$ _____

7. $\dfrac{3}{4} + x = \dfrac{7}{8}$ _____   8. $y - 3\dfrac{1}{2} = -2\dfrac{2}{3}$ _____   9. $48x = -192$ _____

10. $-25a = -200$ _____   11. $-15y = 96$ _____   12. $-\dfrac{1}{3}x = 48$ _____

13. $\dfrac{3}{2}r = -\dfrac{4}{5}$ _____   14. $x - 56 = -42$ _____   15. $15 - y = 33$ _____

16. $51 - x = -133$ _____   17. $-31t = -93$ _____   18. $-53 + a = 65$ _____

19. $-\dfrac{5}{3}b = -\dfrac{1}{6}$ _____   20. $58x = -145$ _____   21. $-89 = -27 - a$ _____

22. $\dfrac{x}{4} = -45$ _____   23. $\dfrac{r}{-3} = \dfrac{1}{3}$ _____   24. $\dfrac{11}{2}y = -3\dfrac{2}{3}$ _____

25. $t + \dfrac{5}{8} = -\dfrac{3}{4}$ _____   26. $\dfrac{b}{-5} = 11$ _____   27. $-\dfrac{7}{8}t = -\dfrac{7}{8}$ _____

28. $3x + 5x = 48$ _____   29. $18x - 12x = -96$ _____

EXTRA PRACTICE 2 (continued)
Solving Linear Equations
Use after Section 1.6

---

30. $3y - 13y = 50$ _____

31. $9t - 16t = -49$ _____

32. $5a - 4 = 26$ _____

33. $8r + 16 = -48$ _____

34. $-10x - 41 = 69$ _____

35. $11b = 45 - 4b$ _____

36. $9z + \dfrac{1}{2}z = 38$ _____

37. $x + 58 = 135$ _____

38. $62y = -558$ _____

39. $3a + 4a - 3 = 11$ _____

40. $6x + 5 - 2x = -19$ _____

41. $9r + 3r - 5 = 25$ _____

42. $3x + 2 = 2x - 6$ _____

43. $5z - 4 = 4z - 3$ _____

44. $4y + 2y - 7 = 3y + 11$ _____

45. $3t - 5 = 7t + t - 15$ _____

46. $6x + 5x - 4 = 2x - 8$ _____

47. $\dfrac{1}{2}x + \dfrac{1}{3}x = \dfrac{1}{6}x - 5$ _____

48. $\dfrac{2}{3}y - \dfrac{5}{4}y + 8 = -\dfrac{11}{12}y - 4$ _____

49. $\dfrac{z}{-5} = -15$ _____

50. $\dfrac{t}{2} = -33$ _____

51. $\dfrac{h}{13} = 0$ _____

52. $-2y + 7 = 7$ _____

53. $5x - 4 = 4x - 4$ _____

54. $-3462a = 0$ _____

EXTRA PRACTICE 3
Solving Formulas
Use after Section 1.6

Name_____

Example: Solve for a.

$$P = 2a + 3b + 4c$$
$$P - 3b - 4c = 2a$$
$$\frac{P - 3b - 4c}{2} = a$$

Solve for the given letter.

1. $A = p + prt$ for r _____

2. $A = p + prt$ for t _____

3. $V = lwh$ for l _____

4. $V = lwh$ for h _____

5. $A = \frac{1}{2}d_1 d_2$ for d_1 _____

6. $A = \frac{1}{2}d_1 d_2$ for d_2 _____

7. $y = mx + b$ for m _____

8. $y = mx + b$ for b _____

9. $p = \frac{100a}{t}$ for a. _____

10. $y = \frac{kx}{z}$ for x _____

11. $A = 2\pi r$ for π _____

12. $V = \pi r^2 h$ for h _____

EXTRA PRACTICE 4
Solving Problems
Use after Section 1.7

Name_____

Solve.

1. When 6 is added to three times a number, the result is 30. Find the number.
   _____

2. When you double a number and then add 20, you get $\frac{4}{3}$ of the original number. Find the number. _____

3. The perimeter of a rectangle is 52 cm. The length is 8 cm greater than the width. Find the width and length. _____

4. The perimeter of a rectangle is 78 m. The width is 7 m less than the length. Find the length and width. _____

5. The sum of three consecutive even integers is 150. Find the integers. _____

6. The sum of three consecutive odd integers is 261. Find the integers. _____

7. A 20-ft board is cut into three pieces. The second piece is three times as long as the first. The third piece is twice as long as the second. Find the lengths of the pieces. _____

8. A 450-m fence is divided into three sections. The second section is twice as long as the first. The third section is three times as long as the second. Find the lengths of the sections. _____

9. The second angle of a triangle is three times as large as the first. The third angle is 20° larger than the sum of the first two. Find the measures of the angles. _____

10. The second angle of a triangle is twice as large as the first. The third angle is 50° less than the second. Find the measures of the angles. _____

11. The cost of renting a car is $18 per day plus 16¢ per mile. Matt pays $214 for a three-day rental. How many miles did he drive? _____

12. Thirteen less than twice a number is seventeen more than half the number. What is the number? _____

EXTRA PRACTICE 5
Finding Function Values
Use after Section 2.1   Name_____

Examples.

Given $f(x) = 3x - 7$, find $f(-2)$.

$f(-2) = 3(-2) - 7 = -6 - 7 = -13$

Given $f(x) = 2x^2 - 5x + 2$, find $f(0)$.

$f(0) = 2(0)^2 - 5(0) + 2 = 2 \cdot 0 - 5 \cdot 0 + 2 = 2$

Given $f(x) = x^3 + 7x - 1$, find $f(3a)$.

$f(3a) = (3a)^3 + 7(3a) - 1 = 27a^3 + 21a - 1$

Find the function values.

1. $f(x) = 2x + 5$

    a) $f(-2) =$ _____

    b) $f(-8) =$ _____

    c) $f(0) =$ _____

    d) $f(1.2) =$ _____

    e) $f\left(\dfrac{3}{4}\right) =$ _____

2. $g(t) = t^2 - 5$

    a) $g(0) =$ _____

    b) $g(7) =$ _____

    c) $g(-9) =$ _____

    d) $g(-1.4) =$ _____

    e) $g\left(\dfrac{2}{3}\right) =$ _____

3. $h(x) = -22$

    a) $h(-11) =$ _____

    b) $h(-1.6) =$ _____

    c) $h(0) =$ _____

    d) $h(15) =$ _____

    e) $h(209) =$ _____

4. $f(x) = |x| - 8$

    a) $f(-19) =$ _____

    b) $f(-1) =$ _____

    c) $f(0) =$ _____

    d) $f(18) =$ _____

    e) $f(100) =$ _____

5. $g(t) = |t - 2|$

    a) $g(7) =$ _____

    b) $g(-5) =$ _____

    c) $g(-30) =$ _____

    d) $g(400) =$ _____

    e) $g(a + 1) =$ _____

6. $f(x) = 2x^3 - x$

    a) $f(0) =$ _____

    b) $f(4) =$ _____

    c) $f(-3) =$ _____

    d) $f(4a) =$ _____

    e) $f(-10) =$ _____

EXTRA PRACTICE 6
Finding Domain and Range
Use after Section 2.1

Name_____

The solutions of an equation in two different variables consist of a set of ordered pairs. The
<u>domain</u> is the set of all first coordinates and the <u>range</u> is the set of all second coordinates.

Find the domain and the range of each of the following functions.

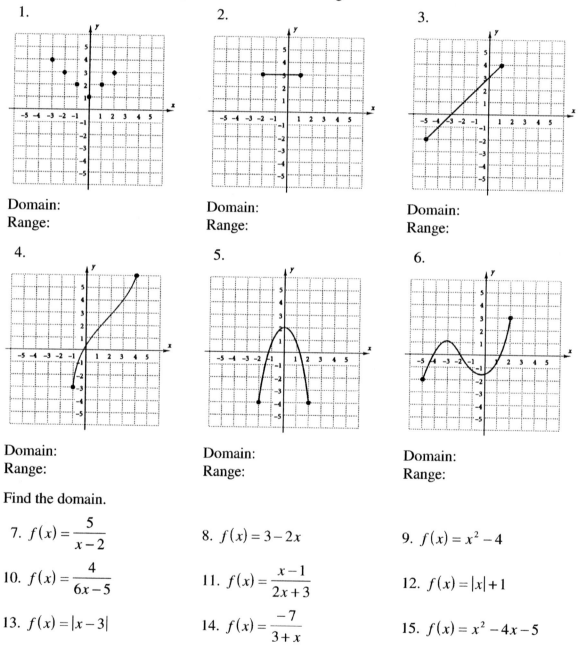

1.

Domain:
Range:

2.

Domain:
Range:

3.

Domain:
Range:

4.

Domain:
Range:

5.

Domain:
Range:

6.

Domain:
Range:

Find the domain.

7. $f(x) = \dfrac{5}{x-2}$

8. $f(x) = 3 - 2x$

9. $f(x) = x^2 - 4$

10. $f(x) = \dfrac{4}{6x-5}$

11. $f(x) = \dfrac{x-1}{2x+3}$

12. $f(x) = |x| + 1$

13. $f(x) = |x-3|$

14. $f(x) = \dfrac{-7}{3+x}$

15. $f(x) = x^2 - 4x - 5$

EXTRA PRACTICE 7
Graphing Linear Equations
Use after Section 2.2

Name_____

Example: Graph. $y = x - 2$

x	y $y = x - 2$	(x, y)
-2	-4	$(-2, -4)$
-1	-3	$(-1, -3)$
0	-2	$(0, -2)$
1	-1	$(1, -1)$
2	0	$(2, 0)$

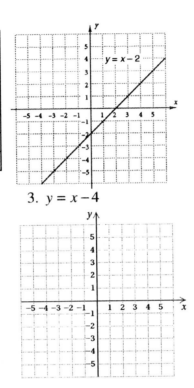

1. $y = 3x + 1$

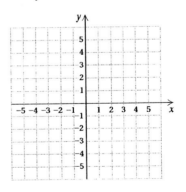

2. $y = 2x - 3$

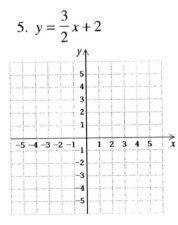

3. $y = x - 4$

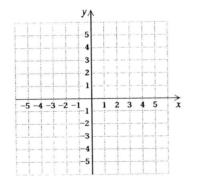

4. $y = -3x + 2$

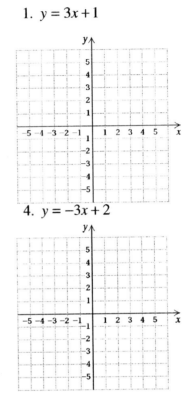

5. $y = \dfrac{3}{2}x + 2$

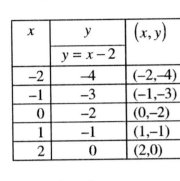

6. $y = -x$

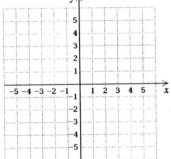

7. $y = x + 5$

EXTRA PRACTICE 7 (continued)
Graphing Linear Equations
Use after Section 2.2

---

8. $y = -3x - 1$

9. $y = 5 - x$

10. $y = \dfrac{2}{3}x - 1$

11. $y = 3x - 2$

12. $y = -4 - x$

13. $y = -3x$

14. $y = 2x + 3$

15. $y = \dfrac{1}{3}x + 2$

16. $y = 5x - 4$

EXTRA PRACTICE 8
More on Graphing Linear Equations
Use after Section 2.3

Name_____

Examples: Graph.
a) $3x - 2y = 6$

To find the y-intercept,
let $x = 0$. Then solve for y:
$$3 \cdot 0 - 2y = 6$$
$$-2y = 6$$
$$y = -3$$

Thus $(0,-3)$ is the y-intercept.
Plot both intercepts and a third
point $(4,3)$ as a check.

To find the x-intercept,
let $y = 0$. Then solve for x:
$$3x - 2 \cdot 0 = 6$$
$$3x = 6$$
$$x = 2$$

Thus $(2,0)$ is the x-intercept.

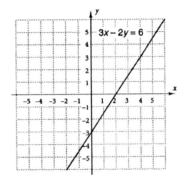

b) $y = -3$

x	y	(x, y)
	$y = -3$	
-2	-3	$(-2,-3)$
0	-3	$(0,-3)$
4	-3	$(4,-3)$

c) $x = 4$

x	y	(x, y)
$x = 4$		
4	-2	$(4,-2)$
4	0	$(4,0)$
4	3	$(4,3)$

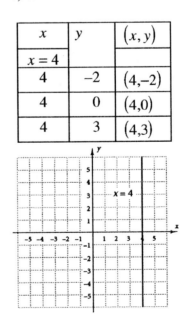

EXTRA PRACTICE 8 (continued)
More on Graphing Linear Equations
Use after Section 2.3

Graph.

1. $3x + 6y = 12$

2. $2x - 5y = 10$

3. $x - 3y = 6$

4. $y = 2$

5. $y = 3x + 1$

6. $4x + 2y = 8$

7. $x - y = 3$

8. $x = -1$

9. $5x + 3y = 15$

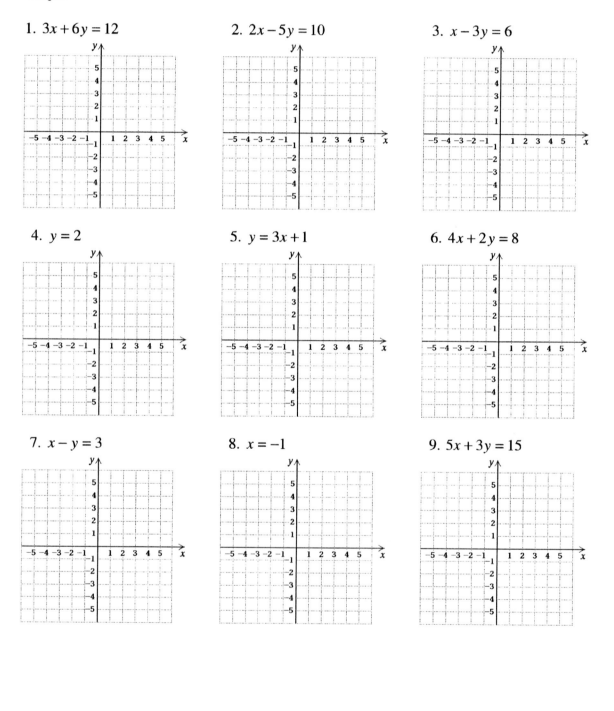

EXTRA PRACTICE 9
Slope and Equations of Lines
Use after Section 2.4   **Name**_____

_____

Examples:

a) Find a slope-intercept equation for the line with slope 2 that contains $(0,5)$.

$y = mx + b$ The slope-intercept equation.

$y = 2x + 5$ Substitute 2 for m and 5 for b.

b) Find an equation of a line that contains the points $(5,-2)$ and $(-2,1)$.

$m = \dfrac{1-(-2)}{-2-5} = \dfrac{3}{-7} = -\dfrac{3}{7}$ First find the slope.

$y - (-2) = -\dfrac{3}{7}(x-5)$ Use the point-slope equation and substitute $-\dfrac{3}{7}$ for m,

5 for x_1, and -2 for y_1.

$y + 2 = -\dfrac{3}{7}x + \dfrac{15}{7}$ (We could just as easily have substituted -2 for x_1 and

1 for y_1.)

$y = -\dfrac{3}{7}x + \dfrac{15}{7} - \dfrac{14}{7}$

$y = -\dfrac{3}{7}x + \dfrac{1}{7}$

We could also use the slope-intercept equation. See Section 2.6 for an example.

Find an equation of the line containing the given point and having the given slope.

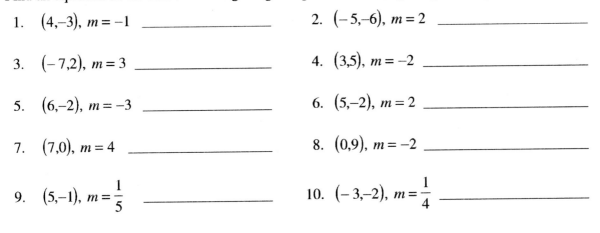

1. $(4,-3)$, $m = -1$ _____

2. $(-5,-6)$, $m = 2$ _____

3. $(-7,2)$, $m = 3$ _____

4. $(3,5)$, $m = -2$ _____

5. $(6,-2)$, $m = -3$ _____

6. $(5,-2)$, $m = 2$ _____

7. $(7,0)$, $m = 4$ _____

8. $(0,9)$, $m = -2$ _____

9. $(5,-1)$, $m = \dfrac{1}{5}$ _____

10. $(-3,-2)$, $m = \dfrac{1}{4}$ _____

EXTRA PRACTICE 9 (continued)
Slope and Equations of Lines
Use after Section 2.4

Find an equation of the line that contains the given pair of points

11. $(1,5)$ and $(4,2)$ _____   12. $(-4,2)$ and $(1,-3)$ _____

13. $(-5,-3)$ and $(1,-1)$ _____   14. $(0,3)$ and $(-2,6)$ _____

15. $(-8,3)$ and $(-4,1)$ _____   16. $(6,2)$ and $(-3,0)$ _____

17. $(1,3)$ and $(4,6)$ _____   18. $(3,-4)$ and $(-3,4)$ _____

19. $(-7,4)$ and $(-4,7)$ _____   20. $(9,-5)$ and $(7,7)$ _____

EXTRA PRACTICE 10
Solving Systems of Linear Equations
Use after Sections 3.2   **Name**_____

_____

Examples:
a)   Solve using the substitution method: $5x - 2y = 4$,
$$y = 5 - x.$$

Substitute $5 - x$ for y.

$$5x - 2y = 4$$
$$5x - 2(5 - x) = 4$$
$$5x - 10 + 2x = 4$$
$$7x = 14$$
$$x = 2$$

Then substitute 2 for x and solve for y.

$$y = 5 - x$$
$$y = 5 - 2$$
$$y = 3$$

The solution is $(2,3)$.

b) Solve using the elimination method: $2x + 7y = -1$,
$$-x - 2y = 2.$$

Multiply the second equation
by 2 and then add.

$$2x + 7y = -1$$
$$\underline{-2x - 4y = 4}$$
$$3y = 3$$
$$y = 1$$

Then substitute 1 for y and solve for x.

$$2x + 7y = -1$$
$$2x + 7 \cdot 1 = -1$$
$$2x + 7 = -1$$
$$2x = -8$$
$$x = -4$$

The solution is $(-4,1)$.

Solve.

1. $4x + 3y = 1$,
     $x = 1 - y$ _____

2. $2x - y = 6$,
     $-x + y = -1$ _____

3. $6x - y = 3$,
     $4x - 2y = -2$ _____

4. $2x + 3y = 7$,
     $x = 1 - 4y$ _____

5. $2x + 3y = 6$,
     $x - 3y = -15$ _____

6. $7x - 5y = 4$,
     $y = 3x - 4$ _____

EXTRA PRACTICE 10 (continued)
Solving Systems of Linear Equations
Use after Sections 3.2

7. $2y - 5x = -1,$
   $x = 2y + 5$ _____

8. $4x + 3y = 1,$
   $3x + 5y = -13$ _____

9. $6x - 5y = 3,$
   $4x + 3y = 21$ _____

10. $x + y = 4,$
    $3x + 4y = 10$ _____

11. $-3x + y = 2,$
    $7x - 8y = 1$ _____

12. $7x + 2y = 2,$
    $x - 2y = 14$ _____

13. $9y - 2x = -7,$
    $x - 3y = 5$ _____

14. $3x - 5y = 8,$
    $4x - 7y = 12$ _____

15. $5x + 2y = 12,$
    $3x - 4y = 2$ _____

16. $x + 4y = 7,$
    $3x + 7y = 6$ _____

17. $5x - 8y = 25,$
    $-x + 4y = -7$ _____

18. $0.5x + 2y = 9,$
    $4x - 15y = 2$ _____

19. $8x - 6y = 0,$
    $x + 9y = \dfrac{13}{4}$ _____

20. $\dfrac{2}{3}x + \dfrac{1}{4}y = 18,$
    $\dfrac{1}{6}x - \dfrac{3}{8}y = -6$ _____

EXTRA PRACTICE 11
Solving Problems Using Systems of Equations
Use after Sections 3.3   **Name**_____

Example: The sum of two numbers is 95. One number is 16 less than twice the other. Find the
numbers.

We let x represent one number and y represent the other number.

We solve the following system.
$$x + y = 95,$$
$$x = 2y - 16.$$

Using the substitution method, we substitute $2y - 16$ for x.

$$x + y = 95$$ Then substitute 37 for y and solve for x.
$$(2y - 16) + y = 95$$ $$x = 2y - 16$$
$$3y - 16 = 95$$ $$x = 2 \cdot 37 - 16$$
$$3y = 111$$ $$x = 58$$
$$y = 37$$ One number is 58, the other is 37.

This system could also have been solved using the elimination method.

$$x + y = 95$$ $$x + y = 95$$ $$x + y = 95$$
$$x = 2y - 16$$ or $$x - 2y = -16$$ or $$-x + 2y = 16$$
$$\overline{3y = 111}$$
$$y = 37$$

Then substitute 37 for y and solve for x.

Solve.

1. Find two numbers whose sum is 49 and whose difference is 13. _____

2. Two angles are supplementary. One angle is 60° more than twice the other. Find the
angles. _____

3. Two angles are complementary. Their difference is 36°. Find the angles. _____

4. The perimeter of a rectangle is 160 cm. The length is 4 cm less than three times the width.
Find the length and the width. _____

EXTRA PRACTICE 11 (continued)
Solving Problems Using Systems of Equations
Use after Sections 3.3

5.   The sum of two numbers is -11. Twice the first number minus the second is 32. Find the numbers._____

6.   The difference between two numbers is 14. Twice the smaller is 7 more than the larger. What are the numbers? _____

7.   The perimeter of a lot is 84 ft. The length exceeds the width by 16 feet. Find the length and the width. _____

8.   The sum of a certain number and a second number is 21. The second number minus the first number is -57. Find the numbers. _____

9.   The perimeter of a rectangular field is 110 feet. The length is 7 feet more than twice the width. Find the dimensions. _____

10.   Two angles are complementary. One angle is 10° less than three times the other. Find the measures of the angles. _____

EXTRA PRACTICE 12
Solving Inequalities
Use after Section 4.1

Name_____

_____

Examples: Solve.

a) $5x - 9 > 6$
   $\quad 5x > 15$
   $\quad\quad x > 3$
The solution set is $\{x|x > 3\}$.

b) $4x + 3 \le 7x + 9$
   $\quad -3x \le 6$
   $\quad\quad x \ge -2$
The solution set is $\{x|x \ge -2\}$.

Solve.

1. $y + 3 > 9$ _____

2. $x - 7 \ge -3$ _____

3. $5x < 35$ _____

4. $3a + 2 \ge 8$ _____

5. $8x + 3 < 7x + 4$ _____

6. $-9y > 63$ _____

7. $5x - 9 \ge 2$ _____

8. $3x + 4 \le -2$ _____

9. $10y - 7 > -2y + 17$ _____

10. $3t - 1 \le 8t + 24$ _____

11. $\dfrac{3}{4}x < 7$ _____

12. $8y - 7 > 3 - 2y$ _____

13. $6y + 5 \ge 4y + 7$ _____

14. $2m - 1 \ge 5m - 7$ _____

EXTRA PRACTICE 12 (continued)
Solving Inequalities
Use after Section 4.1

15. $5 + 6x > 9 - x$ _____

16. $10x + 7 \le 7x - 5$ _____

17. $3x + 1 < 16$ _____

18. $5x - 4 > 21$ _____

19. $8y - 11 \ge 7y + 2$ _____

20. $3m - 4 < 7m - 16$ _____

21. $-3x \le \dfrac{1}{4}$ _____

22. $\dfrac{3}{2}y > -6$ _____

23. $x + 2 \ge 3x - 4$ _____

24. $7x < 2x + 15$ _____

25. $x - \dfrac{1}{2} > \dfrac{1}{3}$ _____

26. $y + \dfrac{2}{3} \le \dfrac{5}{6}$ _____

27. $15 - 3x > 4x - 13$ _____

28. $-2 < 5x + 8 - 3x$ _____

29. $17 < 5 - 4y$ _____

30. $31 > 7 - 6y$ _____

EXTRA PRACTICE 13
Absolute-Value Equations and Inequalities
Use after Section 4.4   **Name**_____

_____

Examples: Solve.

a) $|3x - 5| = 16$

$\quad\quad 3x - 5 = -16 \quad$ or $\; 3x - 5 = 16$

$\quad\quad\quad 3x = -11 \quad$ or $\quad\quad 3x = 21$

$\quad\quad\quad\; x = -\dfrac{11}{3} \quad$ or $\quad\quad\; x = 7$

$\quad$ The solution set is $\left\{ -\dfrac{11}{3}, 7 \right\}$.

b) $|3x - 5| \le 16$

$\quad\quad -16 \le 3x - 5 \le 16$

$\quad\quad -11 \le 3x \le 21$

$\quad\quad -\dfrac{11}{3} \le x \le 7$

$\quad$ The solution set is $\left\{ x \middle| -\dfrac{11}{3} \le x \le 7 \right\}$.

c) $|3x - 5| > 16$

$\quad\quad 3x - 5 < -16 \quad$ or $\; 3x - 5 > 16$

$\quad\quad\;\; 3x < -11 \quad$ or $\; 3x > 21$

$\quad\quad\;\; x < -\dfrac{11}{3} \quad$ or $\; x > 7$

$\quad$ The solution set is $\left\{ x \middle| x < -\dfrac{11}{3} \text{ or } x > 7 \right\}$.

Solve.

1. $|8x - 3| > 21$ _____

2. $|y - 2| \le 7$ _____

3. $|5x + 8| < 23$ _____

4. $|9 - 2x| = 5$ _____

5. $|x| = 4$ _____

6. $\left| \dfrac{1}{2}y - 3 \right| \ge 3$ _____

7. $|y + 9| \le 2$ _____

8. $\left| y + \dfrac{1}{3} \right| > \dfrac{4}{3}$ _____

9. $|-4x + 3| > 13$ _____

10. $\left| \dfrac{5}{8}x \right| < 10$ _____

EXTRA PRACTICE 13 (continued)
Absolute-Value Equations and Inequalities
Use after Section 4.4

11. $|10y - 1.3| = 4.7$ _____

12. $|9 - 4x| \geq 15$ _____

13. $|x + 9| > 17$ _____

14. $\left|\dfrac{3}{4} + x\right| = \dfrac{1}{4}$ _____

15. $|9 - y| > 11$ _____

16. $|y| \leq \dfrac{1}{5}$ _____

17. $\left|\dfrac{3}{7}y\right| > \dfrac{3}{7}$ _____

18. $|3 - x| = 2$ _____

19. $|5x - 2| \geq 15$ _____

20. $|17 - 4x| < 23$ _____

21. $|y - 3| = 51$ _____

22. $|19 - x| > 19$ _____

23. $|8x - 3| \leq 5$ _____

24. $|2y - 9| < 15$ _____

25. $|y| > 9$ _____

26. $\left|3y - \dfrac{5}{9}\right| \leq \dfrac{4}{9}$ _____

27. $|8 - 3y| < 35$ _____

28. $|0.2x + 0.5| \geq 0.9$ _____

29. $\left|x - \dfrac{2}{9}\right| \geq \dfrac{4}{9}$ _____

30. $|34 - 4y| \leq 14$ _____

EXTRA PRACTICE 14
Factoring Polynomials
Use after Sections 5.3   **Name**_____

Examples. Factor completely.

a) $4x^3 + 12x^2 - 8x = 4x(x^2 + 3x - 2)$
b) $5x^3 - 3x^2 + 20x - 12 = x^2(5x - 3) + 4(5x - 3) = (5x - 3)(x^2 + 4)$
c) $x^2 + 2x - 35 = (x + 7)(x - 5)$
d) $3x^2 - 5x - 2 = (3x + 1)(x - 2)$
e) $x^2 - 18x + 81 = (x - 9)^2$
f) $4x^2 - 25y^2 = (2x + 5y)(2x - 5y)$

Factor.

1. $x^2 - 6x - 16 =$ _____

2. $4y^2 + 7y - 2 =$ _____

3. $5a^3 - 25a^2 + 15a =$ _____

4. $9x^2 - 16 =$ _____

5. $x^2 - 64 =$ _____

6. $a^2 + 12a + 27 =$ _____

7. $6x^2 + 12x + 6 =$ _____

8. $x^3 + 2x^2 - 5x - 10 =$ _____

9. $x^2 - 10x + 21 =$ _____

10. $12x^5 - 6x^3 + 3x^2 =$ _____

11. $6y^2 - 54 =$ _____

12. $4y^2 - 17y - 15 =$ _____

13. $6x^2 - 7x + 2 =$ _____

14. $5x^2 - 5 =$ _____

15. $y^5 + 3y^3 + 4y^2 + 12 =$ _____

16. $x^2 - 7x - 18 =$ _____

EXTRA PRACTICE 14 (continued)
Factoring Polynomials
Use after Sections 5.3

17. $x^2 - 8x + 16 =$ _____

18. $a^2 - 9a + 14 =$ _____

19. $49x^2 - 1 =$ _____

20. $8x^4 - 4x^3 + 12x^2 =$ _____

21. $y^2 + 10y + 25 =$ _____

22. $3a^2 + 12a - 3 =$ _____

23. $x^4 - 81 =$ _____

24. $9y^2 - 12y + 4 =$ _____

25. $a^2 + 11a + 30 =$ _____

26. $8t^2 + 2t - 3 =$ _____

27. $75x^2 - 30x + 3 =$ _____

28. $3t^2 - 8t - 3 =$ _____

29. $x^2 + 3x + 8x + 24 =$ _____

30. $y^2 - 22y + 121 =$ _____

31. $x^2 - 2x - 3 =$ _____

32. $4x^2 - 24x + 36 =$ _____

33. $y^2 - 6y + 5 =$ _____

34. $25t^2 - 4 =$ _____

35. $14x^3 - 7x^2 + 21x =$ _____

36. $9x^2 + 42x + 49 =$ _____

37. $9x^2 - 81 =$ _____

38. $12x^2 + 4x - 5 =$ _____

39. $49a^2 - 28a + 4 =$ _____

40. $8x^2 - 29x - 12 =$ _____

EXTRA PRACTICE 15
Addition and Subtraction of Rational Expressions
Use after Section 6.2   **Name**_____

Example: Do this calculation.

$$\frac{5x}{x^2-3x-4}-\frac{2x}{x^2-6x+8}$$

$$=\frac{5x}{(x-4)(x+1)}-\frac{2x}{(x-4)(x-2)}, \text{ LCM }=(x-4)(x-2)(x+1)$$

$$=\frac{5x}{(x-4)(x+1)}\cdot\frac{x-2}{x-2}-\frac{2x}{(x-4)(x-2)}\cdot\frac{x+1}{x+1}$$

$$=\frac{5x(x-2)-2x(x+1)}{(x-4)(x-2)(x+1)}$$

$$=\frac{5x^2-10x-2x^2-2x}{(x-4)(x-2)(x+1)}$$

$$=\frac{3x^2-12x}{(x-4)(x-2)(x+1)}$$

$$=\frac{3x(x-4)}{(x-4)(x-2)(x+1)}$$

$$=\frac{3x}{(x-2)(x+1)}$$

Add or subtract. Simplify.

1. $\dfrac{x-1}{x+3}+\dfrac{x+7}{x+3}$ _____

2. $\dfrac{x-1}{x+6}+\dfrac{x+3}{x-2}$ _____

3. $\dfrac{a^2}{a-4}+\dfrac{16}{4-a}$ _____

4. $\dfrac{4y}{y^2-y-2}-\dfrac{5y}{y^2+y-6}$ _____

5. $\dfrac{3x+2}{x-1}-\dfrac{x+5}{x-1}$ _____

6. $\dfrac{4}{a+2}+\dfrac{a+1}{a^2-4}-\dfrac{3}{a-2}$ _____

7. $\dfrac{y-5}{3y+9}-\dfrac{y+1}{2y+6}$ _____

8. $\dfrac{5}{a}+\dfrac{3}{-a}$ _____

9. $\dfrac{x+1}{x^2-7x+10}+\dfrac{3}{x^2-x-2}$ _____

10. $\dfrac{b-3}{b^2-9}+\dfrac{b+3}{b^2+6b+9}$ _____

_____   _____

EXTRA PRACTICE 15 (continued)
Addition and Subtraction of Rational Expressions
Use after Section 6.2

---

11. $\dfrac{a-5}{a^2-5a}+\dfrac{a+5}{a^2-25}$ _____

12. $\dfrac{y+7}{y^2-49}-\dfrac{3y+1}{49-y^2}$ _____

13. $\dfrac{x+2}{x^2+x}-\dfrac{1}{x}+\dfrac{3}{x+1}$ _____

14. $\dfrac{b+3}{2b+6}-\dfrac{2}{3b}$ _____

15. $\dfrac{5x}{x+2}-\dfrac{x}{x-1}+\dfrac{3}{x^2+x-2}$

16. $\dfrac{5}{x^2+3x}-\dfrac{4}{x^2-x-12}$

_____

_____

17. $\dfrac{a}{1-a}+\dfrac{3a}{a+1}-\dfrac{5}{a^2-1}$

18. $\dfrac{8x+4}{2x^2-9x-5}+\dfrac{x-1}{x-5}$

_____

_____

19. $\dfrac{y-5}{6y}-\dfrac{4y+1}{y}$ _____

20. $\dfrac{9x}{x^2-81}+\dfrac{3x}{x+9}$ _____

EXTRA PRACTICE 16
Simplifying Complex Rational Expressions
Use after Section 6.3

Name_____

Example: Simplify.

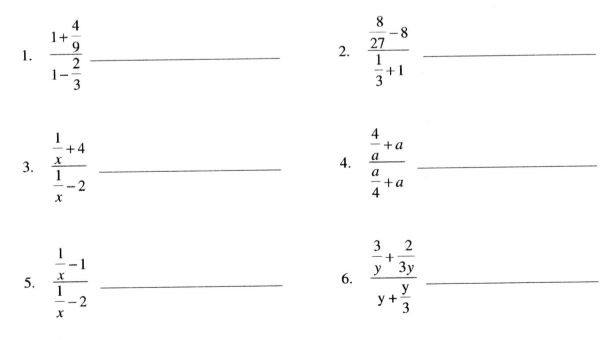

$$\frac{3-\dfrac{1}{x}}{9-\dfrac{1}{x^2}} = \frac{3-\dfrac{1}{x}}{9-\dfrac{1}{x^2}}\cdot\frac{x^2}{x^2}$$

or

$$\frac{3-\dfrac{1}{x}}{9-\dfrac{1}{x^2}} = \frac{3\cdot\dfrac{x}{x}-\dfrac{1}{x}}{9\cdot\dfrac{x^2}{x^2}-\dfrac{1}{x^2}}$$

$$=\frac{3\cdot x^2 - \dfrac{1}{x}\cdot x^2}{9\cdot x^2 - \dfrac{1}{x^2}\cdot x^2}$$

$$=\frac{\dfrac{3x-1}{x}}{\dfrac{9x^2-1}{x^2}}$$

$$=\frac{3x^2-x}{9x^2-1}$$

$$=\frac{3x-1}{x}\cdot\frac{x^2}{9x^2-1}$$

$$=\frac{x(3x-1)}{(3x-1)(3x+1)}$$

$$=\frac{3x-1}{x}\cdot\frac{x^2}{(3x-1)(3x+1)}$$

$$=\frac{x}{3x+1}$$

$$=\frac{x}{3x+1}$$

Simplify.

1. $\dfrac{1+\dfrac{4}{9}}{1-\dfrac{2}{3}}$ _____

2. $\dfrac{\dfrac{8}{27}-8}{\dfrac{1}{3}+1}$ _____

3. $\dfrac{\dfrac{1}{x}+4}{\dfrac{1}{x}-2}$ _____

4. $\dfrac{\dfrac{4}{a}+a}{\dfrac{a}{4}+a}$ _____

5. $\dfrac{\dfrac{1}{x}-1}{\dfrac{1}{x}-2}$ _____

6. $\dfrac{\dfrac{3}{y}+\dfrac{2}{3y}}{y+\dfrac{y}{3}}$ _____

EXTRA PRACTICE 16 (continued)
Simplifying Complex Rational Expressions
Use after Section 6.3

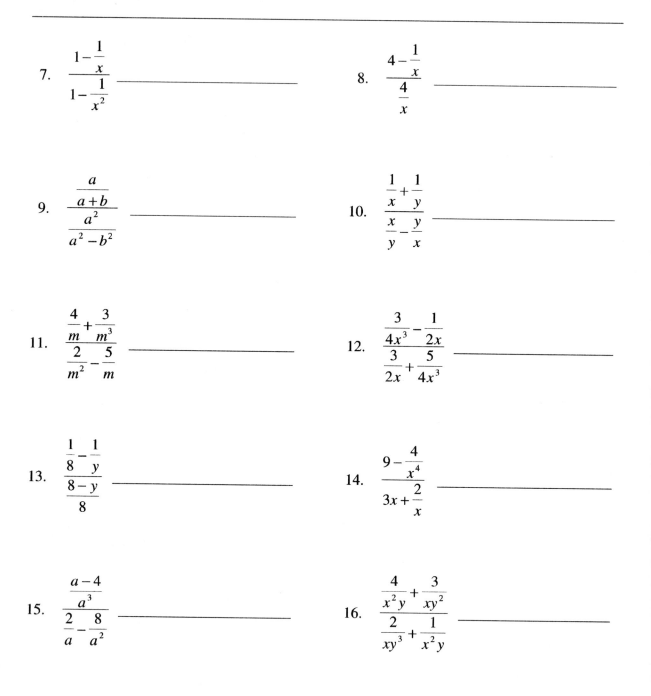

7. $\dfrac{1-\dfrac{1}{x}}{1-\dfrac{1}{x^2}}$ _____

8. $\dfrac{4-\dfrac{1}{x}}{\dfrac{4}{x}}$ _____

9. $\dfrac{\dfrac{a}{a+b}}{\dfrac{a^2}{a^2-b^2}}$ _____

10. $\dfrac{\dfrac{1}{x}+\dfrac{1}{y}}{\dfrac{x}{y}-\dfrac{y}{x}}$ _____

11. $\dfrac{\dfrac{4}{m}+\dfrac{3}{m^3}}{\dfrac{2}{m^2}-\dfrac{5}{m}}$ _____

12. $\dfrac{\dfrac{3}{4x^3}-\dfrac{1}{2x}}{\dfrac{3}{2x}+\dfrac{5}{4x^3}}$ _____

13. $\dfrac{\dfrac{1}{8}-\dfrac{1}{y}}{\dfrac{8-y}{8}}$ _____

14. $\dfrac{9-\dfrac{4}{x^4}}{3x+\dfrac{2}{x}}$ _____

15. $\dfrac{\dfrac{a-4}{a^3}}{\dfrac{2}{a}-\dfrac{8}{a^2}}$ _____

16. $\dfrac{\dfrac{4}{x^2y}+\dfrac{3}{xy^2}}{\dfrac{2}{xy^3}+\dfrac{1}{x^2y}}$ _____

EXTRA PRACTICE 17
Solving Rational Equations
Use after Section 6.4   Name_____

_____

Example: Solve. $\dfrac{5}{x+2} = \dfrac{3}{x}$ Check: $\dfrac{5}{x+2} = \dfrac{3}{x}$

The LCM is $x(x+2)$

$$x(x+2)\left(\dfrac{5}{x+2}\right) = x(x+2)\left(\dfrac{3}{x}\right)$$

$$5x = 3(x+2)$$
$$5x = 3x + 6$$
$$2x = 6$$
$$x = 3$$

$\dfrac{5}{3+2}$	$\dfrac{3}{3}$
$\dfrac{5}{5}$	1
1	

TRUE

The solution is 3.

Solve.

1. $\dfrac{4}{x-1} = \dfrac{5}{x}$ _____

2. $\dfrac{x-3}{x+2} = \dfrac{4}{5}$ _____

3. $\dfrac{5}{x} = \dfrac{4}{x} + \dfrac{1}{2}$ _____

4. $\dfrac{1}{3} - \dfrac{3}{4} = \dfrac{x}{12}$ _____

5. $\dfrac{4}{3x} + \dfrac{2}{x} = \dfrac{2}{3}$ _____

6. $\dfrac{8}{x-5} = \dfrac{2}{x+5}$ _____

7. $\dfrac{x-7}{x+3} = \dfrac{2x}{x+3}$ _____

8. $\dfrac{y-1}{4} - \dfrac{y+1}{10} = 1$ _____

EXTRA PRACTICE 17 (continued)
Solving Rational Equations
Use after Section 6.4

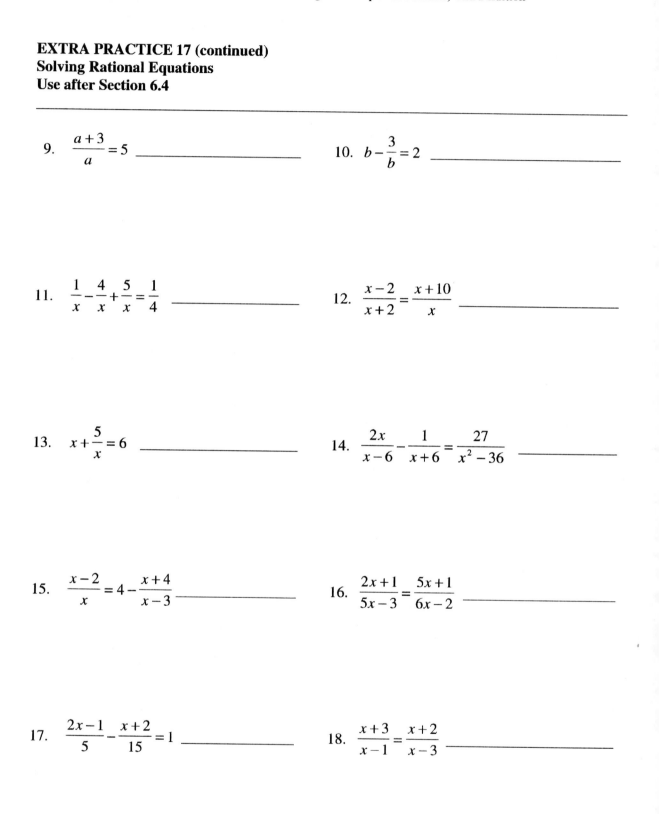

9. $\dfrac{a+3}{a}=5$ _____

10. $b-\dfrac{3}{b}=2$ _____

11. $\dfrac{1}{x}-\dfrac{4}{x}+\dfrac{5}{x}=\dfrac{1}{4}$ _____

12. $\dfrac{x-2}{x+2}=\dfrac{x+10}{x}$ _____

13. $x+\dfrac{5}{x}=6$ _____

14. $\dfrac{2x}{x-6}-\dfrac{1}{x+6}=\dfrac{27}{x^2-36}$ _____

15. $\dfrac{x-2}{x}=4-\dfrac{x+4}{x-3}$ _____

16. $\dfrac{2x+1}{5x-3}=\dfrac{5x+1}{6x-2}$ _____

17. $\dfrac{2x-1}{5}-\dfrac{x+2}{15}=1$ _____

18. $\dfrac{x+3}{x-1}=\dfrac{x+2}{x-3}$ _____

EXTRA PRACTICE 18
Solving Problems and Proportions
Use after Section 6.5   **Name**_____

Example: A number plus five times its reciprocal is -6. Find the number.

A number plus five times its reciprocal is -6.

$$x \quad + \quad 5 \quad \cdot \quad \frac{1}{x} \quad = -6$$

Solve: $x + 5 \cdot \dfrac{1}{x} = -6$

$x\left(x + \dfrac{5}{x}\right) = x(-6)$ Multiplying by the LCD, x, on both sides.

$x^2 + 5 = -6x$

$x^2 + 6x + 5 = 0$

$(x+5)(x+1) = 0$

$x = -5$ or $x = -1$

The values -5 and -1 check in the original problem. The solutions are -5 and -1.

Solve.

1. A number minus three times its reciprocal is 2. Find the number. _____

2. The sum of a number and twice its reciprocal is 3. Find the number. _____

3. It takes Carolyn 4 hr to type a final exam. It takes Elise 3 hr to do the same job. How long would it take them, working together, to do the typing? _____

4. A swimming pool can be filled in 15 hr by pipe A alone and in 24 hr by pipe B alone. How long would it take to fill the pool if both pipes were working? _____

5. One car travels 30 km/h faster than another. In the same time that one travels 200 km, the other goes 320 km. Find their speeds. _____

EXTRA PRACTICE 18 (continued)
Solving Problems and Proportions
Use after Section 6.5

6. The speed of a freight train is 16 mph slower than the speed of a passenger train. The freight train travels 420 miles in the same time that it takes the passenger train to travel 500 miles. Find the speed of each train. _____

7. William walked 195 km in 12 days. At this rate, how far would he walk in 36 days? _____

8. The winner of an election for class president won by a vote of 8 to 5 with 992 votes. How many votes did the loser get? _____

9. Triangles ABC and XYZ are similar. Solve for z if $x = 12$, $a = 10$, and $c = 8$. _____

10. Triangles DEF and GHI are similar. Solve for e if $d = 15$, $g = 9$, and $h = 6$. _____

11. To determine the number of deer in a game preserve, a game warden catches 415 deer, tags them, and lets them loose. Later, 140 deer are caught; 28 of them are tagged. Estimate the number of deer in the preserve. _____

EXTRA PRACTICE 19
Division of Polynomials
Use after Section 6.6   Name_____

Examples: Divide.

a)
$$\left(15x^6 - 10x^4 + 35x^3\right) \div 5x^3$$
$$\frac{15x^6 - 10x^4 + 35x^3}{5x^3}$$
$$= \frac{15x^6}{5x^3} - \frac{10x^4}{5x^3} + \frac{35x^3}{5x^3}$$
$$= 3x^3 - 2x + 7$$

Answer: $3x^3 - 2x + 7$

b)
$$\left(x^4 - 2x^2 + 5x - 6\right) \div (x + 2)$$

$$
\begin{array}{r}
x^3 - 2x^2 + 2x + 1 \\
x+2\overline{)x^4 + 0x^3 - 2x^2 + 5x - 6} \\
\underline{x^4 + 2x^3} \\
-2x^3 - 2x^2 \\
\underline{-2x^3 - 4x^2} \\
2x^2 + 5x \\
\underline{2x^2 + 4x} \\
x - 6 \\
\underline{x + 2} \\
-8
\end{array}
$$

Answer: $x^3 - 2x^2 + 2x + 1$, R -8, or

$$x^3 - 2x^2 + 2x + 1 + \frac{-8}{x+2}$$

We could also use synthetic division in Example (b). See Section 5.3 for an example.
Divide.

1. $\dfrac{32x^4 - 4x^2}{8} = $ _____

2. $\dfrac{3x^5 + 30x^3 + 18x}{6} = $ _____

3. $\dfrac{y - 4y^2 + y^4}{y} = $ _____

4. $\dfrac{27x^8 - 15x^4 + 3x^2}{x^2} = $ _____

5. $\left(25x^7 - 20x^4 + 15x^2\right) \div \left(-5x^2\right) = $

_____

6. $\left(36y^5 + 27y^4 - 18y^3\right) \div \left(9y^2\right) = $

_____

7. $\dfrac{8r^2s^2 + 10rs^3 - 6r^2s}{-2rs} = $ _____

8. $\dfrac{7x^3y^2 - 21x^2y + 35x^3y^4}{7x^2y} = $ _____

EXTRA PRACTICE 19 (continued)
Division of Polynomials
Use after Section 6.6

9. $(x^2 + 3x - 28) \div (x - 4) =$

10. $(x^2 - 16x + 64) \div (x - 8) =$

11. $\dfrac{x^2 - 81}{x + 9} =$ _____

12. $\dfrac{x^2 - 121}{x - 11} =$ _____

13. $(x^2 + 7x + 15) \div (x - 5) =$

14. $(x^2 + 12x - 18) \div (x - 3) =$

15. $\dfrac{10x^3 - 11x^2 + 19x + 10}{5x + 2} =$

16. $\dfrac{12x^3 - 16x^2 - 27x + 36}{3x - 4} =$

17. $(x^4 - 2x^2 + 3) \div (x - 1) =$

18. $(x^4 + 5x^2 + 2) \div (x + 2) =$

19. $(x^6 - 5x^3 - 36) \div (x^3 + 4) =$

20. $(x^6 + 2x^3 - 10) \div (x^3 - 2) =$

21. $(x^4 - 81) \div (x + 3) =$

22. $(x^3 - 64) \div (x - 4) =$

23. $(a^3 - 5a^2 + 25a - 125) \div (a - 5) =$

24. $(a^3 - 5a^2 + 25a - 125) \div (a + 5) =$

EXTRA PRACTICE 20
Multiplying, Dividing, and Simplifying Radical Expressions
Use after Section 7.3 and 7.4   **Name**_____

Examples: Simplify. Assume that all expressions represent nonnegative numbers.

a) $\sqrt[3]{320x^6y^4z^2}$

$= \sqrt[3]{64\cdot 5\cdot x^6\cdot y^3\cdot y\cdot z^2}$

$= \sqrt[3]{64x^6y^3}\sqrt[3]{5yz^2}$

$= 4x^2y\sqrt[3]{5yz^2}$

b) $\sqrt[4]{\left(81a^8b^4\right)^2}$

$= \left(\sqrt[4]{3^4a^8b^4}\right)^2$

$= \left(3a^2b\right)^2$

$= 9a^4b^2$

c) $\sqrt{\dfrac{75y^5}{16x^2}}$

$= \dfrac{\sqrt{75y^5}}{\sqrt{16x^2}}$

$= \dfrac{\sqrt{25y^4\cdot 3y}}{\sqrt{16x^2}}$

$= \dfrac{5y^2\sqrt{3y}}{4x}$

Simplify. Assume that all expressions represent nonnegative numbers.

1. $\sqrt{20x^3yz^2} =$ _____

2. $\sqrt[3]{128x^4y^2} =$ _____

3. $\sqrt[4]{a^{16}b^{12}} =$ _____

4. $\sqrt{\dfrac{49a^3}{b^4}} =$ _____

5. $\sqrt{45a^3bc^2} =$ _____

6. $\sqrt{16^3} =$ _____

7. $\sqrt[3]{\dfrac{16x^5}{y^6}} =$ _____

8. $\sqrt[4]{64a^7b^{12}} =$ _____

9. $\sqrt{50a^2b^5} =$ _____

10. $\sqrt[5]{\left(32x^{10}\right)^3} =$ _____

11. $\sqrt{\dfrac{16x^3}{81}} =$ _____

12. $\sqrt{500x^2yz^{11}} =$ _____

13. $\sqrt[3]{216^2} =$ _____

14. $\sqrt[3]{\dfrac{64a^7}{27}} =$ _____

15. $\sqrt[3]{240x^4y^5} =$ _____

16. $\sqrt[4]{x^7y^9z^{12}} =$ _____

17. $\sqrt{\dfrac{24x^3}{25}} =$ _____

18. $\sqrt[4]{256^3} =$ _____

19. $\sqrt[5]{\left(32a^5b^{10}\right)^3} =$ _____

20. $\sqrt[3]{\left(54a^3\right)^2} =$ _____

EXTRA PRACTICE 20 (continued)
Multiplying, Dividing, and Simplifying Radical Expressions
Use after Section 7.3 and 7.4

Examples: Assume that all expressions represent nonnegative numbers.

a) Multiply and simplify.

$$\sqrt{32xy^3}\,\sqrt{4x^2y^5}$$

$$=\sqrt{128x^3y^8}$$

$$=\sqrt{64\cdot2\cdot x^2\cdot x\cdot y^8}$$

$$=\sqrt{64x^2y^8}\,\sqrt{2x}$$

$$=8xy^4\sqrt{2x}$$

b)   Divide and simplify.

$$\frac{\sqrt[3]{56a^5b^{14}}}{\sqrt[3]{7ab^5}}$$

$$=\sqrt[3]{\frac{56a^5b^{14}}{7ab^5}}$$

$$=\sqrt[3]{8a^4b^9}$$

$$=\sqrt[3]{8\cdot a^3\cdot a\cdot b^9}=2ab^3\sqrt[3]{a}$$

Multiply or divide and simplify. Assume that all expressions represent nonnegative numbers.

21. $\sqrt[3]{5(x+2)^2}\,\sqrt[3]{25(x+2)^2}=$ _____

22. $\dfrac{\sqrt{32a^5b^3}}{\sqrt{2ab^2}}=$ _____

23. $\dfrac{6\sqrt{45x^3}}{3\sqrt{5x}}=$ _____

24. $\sqrt[3]{x^7}\,\sqrt[3]{64xy^2}=$ _____

25. $\sqrt{8x^3y}\,\sqrt{3xy^2}=$ _____

26. $\dfrac{\sqrt[3]{81a^5b^8}}{\sqrt[3]{3ab^2}}=$ _____

27. $\dfrac{\sqrt[3]{625x^6y^4}}{\sqrt[3]{5xy}}=$ _____

28. $\sqrt{6(x+3)^3}\,\sqrt{3(x+3)}=$ _____

29. $\sqrt[3]{6^5a^2b}\,\sqrt[3]{6^2ab}=$ _____

30. $\dfrac{\sqrt[3]{27xy^7}}{\sqrt[3]{xy}}=$ _____

31. $\dfrac{9\,\sqrt[5]{160x^8y^{11}}}{3\,\sqrt[5]{5xy^2}}=$ _____

32. $\sqrt[3]{4(y-3)^2}\,\sqrt[3]{2(y-3)^5}=$ _____

EXTRA PRACTICE 21
Rationalizing Denominators
Use after Section 7.5

Name_____

Examples: Assume that all expressions represent nonnegative numbers.

a) Rationalize the denominator.

$$\frac{\sqrt[3]{4x^2}}{\sqrt[3]{2y^5}}$$

$$= \frac{\sqrt[3]{4x^2}}{\sqrt[3]{3y^5}} \cdot \frac{\sqrt[3]{9y}}{\sqrt[3]{9y}}$$

$$= \frac{\sqrt[3]{36x^2y}}{\sqrt[3]{27y^6}}$$

$$= \frac{\sqrt[3]{36x^2y}}{3y^2}$$

b) Rationalize the denominator.

$$\frac{5}{\sqrt{7}+\sqrt{5}}$$

$$= \frac{5}{\sqrt{7}+\sqrt{5}} \cdot \frac{\sqrt{7}-\sqrt{5}}{\sqrt{7}-\sqrt{5}}$$

$$= \frac{5\sqrt{7}-5\sqrt{5}}{\left(\sqrt{7}\right)^2 - \left(\sqrt{5}\right)^2}$$

$$= \frac{5\sqrt{7}-5\sqrt{5}}{7-5}$$

$$= \frac{5\sqrt{7}-5\sqrt{5}}{2}$$

Rationalize the denominator. Assume that all expressions represent nonnegative numbers.

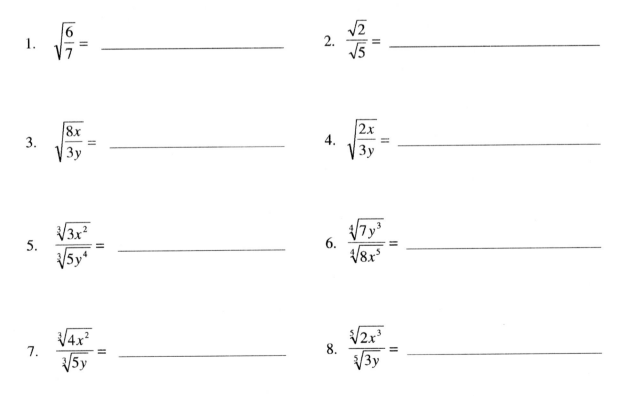

1. $\sqrt{\dfrac{6}{7}} =$ _____

2. $\dfrac{\sqrt{2}}{\sqrt{5}} =$ _____

3. $\sqrt{\dfrac{8x}{3y}} =$ _____

4. $\sqrt{\dfrac{2x}{3y}} =$ _____

5. $\dfrac{\sqrt[3]{3x^2}}{\sqrt[3]{5y^4}} =$ _____

6. $\dfrac{\sqrt[4]{7y^3}}{\sqrt[4]{8x^5}} =$ _____

7. $\dfrac{\sqrt[3]{4x^2}}{\sqrt[3]{5y}} =$ _____

8. $\dfrac{\sqrt[5]{2x^3}}{\sqrt[5]{3y}} =$ _____

EXTRA PRACTICE 21 (continued)
Rationalizing Denominators
Use after Section 7.5

9. $\dfrac{\sqrt[3]{3x}}{\sqrt[3]{y}} =$ _____

10. $\sqrt{\dfrac{5y}{3x}} =$ _____

11. $\dfrac{2x}{\sqrt{5y}} =$ _____

12. $\dfrac{3x^2}{\sqrt[3]{2y}} =$ _____

13. $\dfrac{4}{8 - \sqrt{5}} =$ _____

14. $\dfrac{-3\sqrt{5}}{\sqrt{6} - \sqrt{3}} =$ _____

15. $\dfrac{18\sqrt{3}}{\sqrt{3} - \sqrt{7}} =$ _____

16. $\dfrac{2\sqrt{3}}{\sqrt{3x} - \sqrt{2x}} =$ _____

17. $\dfrac{\sqrt{7} - 2\sqrt{3}}{\sqrt{7} - \sqrt{3}} =$ _____

18. $\dfrac{2\sqrt{x} - \sqrt{y}}{\sqrt{x} + \sqrt{y}} =$ _____

19. $\dfrac{\sqrt{7} - 2\sqrt{x}}{\sqrt{7} + \sqrt{x}} =$ _____

20. $\dfrac{2\sqrt{x} - \sqrt{y}}{\sqrt{x} - 3\sqrt{y}} =$ _____

EXTRA PRACTICE 22
Solving Radical Equations
Use after Section 7.6　　　　　　　　**Name**_____

Example: Solve.

$\sqrt{x+19} - \sqrt{x-20} = 3$　　　　　Check:

$$\sqrt{x+19} = \sqrt{x-20} + 3$$
$$\left(\sqrt{x+19}\right)^2 = \left(\sqrt{x-20} + 3\right)^2$$
$$x+19 = x-20+6\sqrt{x-20} + 9$$
$$30 = 6\sqrt{x-20}$$
$$5 = \sqrt{x-20}$$
$$5^2 = \left(\sqrt{x-20}\right)^2$$
$$25 = x-20$$
$$45 = x$$

$$\sqrt{x+19} - \sqrt{x-20} = 3$$
$$\begin{array}{c|c} \sqrt{45+19} - \sqrt{45-20} & 3 \\ \sqrt{64} - \sqrt{25} & \\ 8-5 & \\ 3 & \text{TRUE} \end{array}$$

The solution is 45.

Solve.

1.　$x+2 = \sqrt{7x+2}$ _____

2.　$\sqrt{x} - 3 = 3$ _____

3.　$\sqrt{x+9} + \sqrt{x+2} = 7$ _____

4.　$y-5 = \sqrt{y-3}$ _____

5.　$\sqrt{-3x+4} = 2 - x$ _____

6.　$1-x = \sqrt{-5x+1}$ _____

7.　$\sqrt{a} + 2 = 5$ _____

8.　$\sqrt{x-5} + \sqrt{x+6} = 11$ _____

EXTRA PRACTICE 22 (continued)
Solving Radical Equations
Use after Section 7.6

9. $\sqrt[3]{x-1} - 3 = 0$ _____

10. $\sqrt{y+3} - \sqrt{2y-8} = 1$ _____

11. $\sqrt{x+12} - \sqrt{x-12} = 12$ _____

12. $\sqrt{x+4} - \sqrt{2x+9} = -1$ _____

13. $\sqrt{x+7} + \sqrt{x-4} = 11$ _____

14. $5 - \sqrt{x} = 1$ _____

15. $\sqrt[3]{4x+3} + 2 = 5$ _____

16. $\sqrt{x+9} + \sqrt{x+4} = 5$ _____

17. $\sqrt{x+10} + \sqrt{x} = 3$ _____

18. $\sqrt{5x+3} = \sqrt{3x+7}$ _____

19. $\sqrt{7x+8} - \sqrt{41-2x} = 3$ _____

20. $\sqrt{10-2x} - \sqrt{5x+16} = 3$ _____

EXTRA PRACTICE 23
Solving Quadratic Equations Using the Quadratic Formula
Use after Section 8.2   **Name**_____

Example: Solve $3x^2 - 5x + 1 = 0$ using the quadratic formula.

$$3x^2 - 5x + 1 = 0$$

$$a = 3 \quad b = -5 \quad c = 1$$

$$x = \frac{-(-5) \pm \sqrt{(-5)^2 - 4(3)(1)}}{2(3)}$$

$$= \frac{5 \pm \sqrt{25 - 12}}{6} = \frac{5 \pm \sqrt{13}}{6}$$

$$\left[\text{Quadratic formula:} \quad x = \frac{-b \pm \sqrt{b^2 - 4ac}}{2a} \right]$$

Solve.

1. $x^2 - 3x = 4$ _____

2. $y^2 - 6y = -8$ _____

3. $x^2 = 10x - 25$ _____

4. $2y^2 - 7y - 15 = 0$ _____

5. $x^2 - 36 = 0$ _____

6. $y^2 - 49 = 0$ _____

7. $x^2 - 3x - 3 = 0$ _____

8. $x^2 - 5x - 7 = 0$ _____

9. $y^2 - 8y + 11 = 0$ _____

10. $y^2 + 7y - 1 = 0$ _____

EXTRA PRACTICE 23 (continued)
Solving Quadratic Equations Using the Quadratic Formula
Use after Section 8.2

11. $x^2 + 6x + 8 = 4$ _____

12. $x^2 - 3x + 1 = 6$ _____

13. $4x^2 + 7x + 2 = 0$ _____

14. $5x^2 - 3x - 1 = 0$ _____

15. $2x^2 - 3x = 3$ _____

16. $6x^2 + 6x = 8$ _____

17. $4y^2 - 6y - 1 = 0$ _____

18. $2y^2 - 5y = -3$ _____

19. $8x^2 = 200$ _____

20. $9x^2 = 144$ _____

EXTRA PRACTICE 24
Solving Problems Using Quadratic Equations
Use after Section 8.3   **Name**_____

Example: Find the length of a diagonal of a square whose sides are 7 m long. Give an exact
answer and an approximation to three decimal places.

Let d = length of the diagonal.
Then substitute 7 for a, 7 for b, and d for c in the Pythagorean equation.

$$7^2 + 7^2 = d^2$$
$$49 + 49 = d^2$$
$$98 = d^2$$
$$\sqrt{98} = d$$
$$9.899 \approx d$$

The length of the diagonal is $\sqrt{98}$ m, or approximately 9.899 m.

Solve.

1. Find the length of a diagonal of a square whose sides are 11 cm long. _____

2. Find the length of a diagonal of a rectangle with width 9 cm and length 12 cm.

   _____

3. The width of a rectangle is 5 inches less than its length. The area of the rectangle is 84 in.^{2}.
   Find the dimensions of the rectangle. _____

4. The hypotenuse of a right triangle is 50 m long. The length of one leg is 10 m longer than
   the other. Find the length of the shorter leg. _____

5. The length of a rectangle is 4 times the width. The area of the rectangle is 900 in.^{2}. Find
   the length and the width. _____

6. The hypotenuse of a right triangle is 17 feet. One leg is 7 feet shorter than the other. Find
   the lengths of the legs. _____

EXTRA PRACTICE 24 (continued)
Solving Problems Using Quadratic Equations
Use after Section 8.3

7. The length of a rectangle is 5 inches more than twice the width. The area of the rectangle is 102 in.^{2}. How long is the rectangle? _____

8. The hypotenuse of a right triangle is 26 in. The length of one leg is 14 in. longer than the other. Find the length of the shorter leg. _____

9. The perimeter of a rectangle is 20 inches. The area of the same rectangle is 18 sq. inches. Find the width of the rectangle to the nearest tenth of an inch. _____

10. A landscaper wants to enclose a 90-ft by 120-ft rectangle with a walk of uniform width. He wants to use a supply of crushed rock that will cover 1744 square feet of walk. How wide should he make the walk? _____

11. A boat travels 12 miles upstream and then turns around and travels 12 miles downstream. The total time for both trips is 3 hours. If the stream flows at 1 mph, how fast does the boat travel in still water? Round the answer to the nearest tenth. _____

12. The speed of a boat in still water is 15 km/h. The boat travels 40 km upstream and 40 km downstream in a total time of 6 hr. What is the speed of the stream? _____

EXTRA PRACTICE 25
Solving Equations Quadratic in Form
Use after Section 8.5   **Name**_____

Example: Solve. $\left(1+3\sqrt{x}\right)^2 - 11\left(1+3\sqrt{x}\right) + 28 = 0$

   Let $u = 1 + 3\sqrt{x}$ and substitute u for $1 + 3\sqrt{x}$.
   $u^2 - 11u + 28 = 0$
   $(u-7)(u-4) = 0$
   $u - 7 = 0$ or $u - 4 = 0$
      $u = 7$ or $u = 4$

   Substitute $1 + 3\sqrt{x}$ for u and solve for x.
   $1 + 3\sqrt{x} = 7$ or $1 + 3\sqrt{x} = 4$
      $3\sqrt{x} = 6$ or $3\sqrt{x} = 3$
       $\sqrt{x} = 2$ or $\sqrt{x} = 1$
        $x = 4$ or $x = 1$

   Both values check. The solutions are 4 and 1.

Solve.

1. $a - 6\sqrt{a} - 27 = 0$ _____

2. $x^4 - 8x^2 + 12 = 0$ _____

3. $5x^{-2} - 5x^{-1} - 60 = 0$ _____

4. $(3x-1)^2 + 2(3x-1) - 15 = 0$ _____

5. $a - 10\sqrt{a} + 9 = 0$ _____

6. $\left(5-\sqrt{x}\right)^2 + 5\left(5-\sqrt{x}\right) - 24 = 0$ _____

EXTRA PRACTICE 25 (continued)
Solving Equations Quadratic in Form
Use after Section 8.5

7. $x^4 - 6x^2 + 8 = 0$ _____

8. $x - 13\sqrt{x} + 36 = 0$ _____

9. $\left(y^2 - 2y\right)^2 - 11\left(y^2 - 2y\right) + 24 = 0$

_____

10. $x^4 + 4x^2 - 21 = 0$ _____

11. $\left(x^2 - 5x\right)^2 - 2\left(x^2 - 5x\right) - 24 = 0$

_____

12. $a - 12\sqrt{a} + 20 = 0$ _____

13. $(4x + 2)^2 - 10(4x + 2) + 25 = 0$

_____

14. $\left(\sqrt{x} - 7\right)^2 - 13\left(\sqrt{x} - 7\right) + 40 = 0$

_____

15. $x^4 - 7x^2 + 12 = 0$ _____

16. $2y^{-2} + 7y^{-1} - 15 = 0$ _____

EXTRA PRACTICE 26
Graphs of Quadratic Functions
Use after Sections 8.6 and 8.7

Name_____

See Sections 8.6 and 8.7 for examples.

1. $f(x) = 3x^2$

2. $f(x) = (x-1)^2$

3. $f(x) = (x-2)^2 + 3$

4. $f(x) = 2(x-3)^2 + 1$

5. $f(x) = x^2 - 6x + 7$

6. $f(x) = -4x^2$

7. $f(x) = x^2 + 4x + 2$

8. $f(x) = 3(x-1)^2$

9. $f(x) = -2x^2 - 20x - 47$

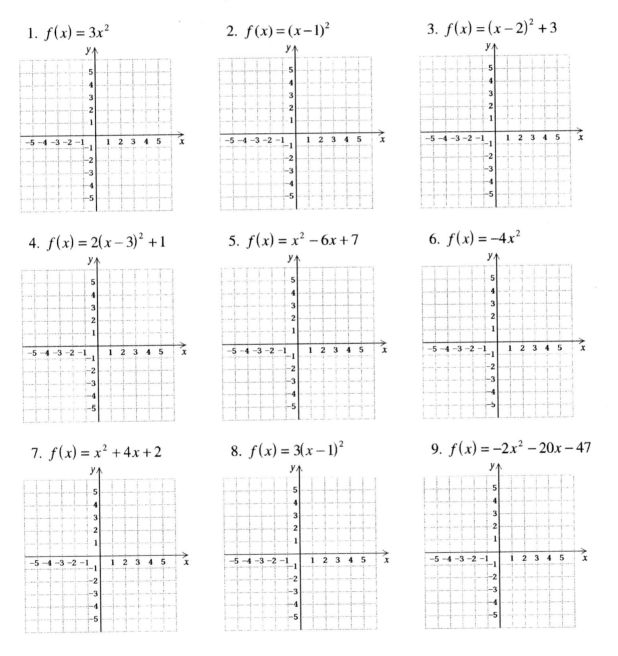

EXTRA PRACTICE 26 (continued)
Graphs of Quadratic Functions
Use after Sections 8.6 and 8.7

10. $f(x) = (x+3)^2$

11. $f(x) = -\dfrac{1}{2}x^2$

12. $f(x) = (x-1)^2 - 2$

13. $f(x) = 2x^2 - 16x + 29$

14. $f(x) = 2(x-1)^2$

15. $f(x) = (x-3)^2$

16. $f(x) = 1.5x^2$

17. $f(x) = -2(x+3)^2 + 4$

18. $f(x) = x^2 - 2x + 3$

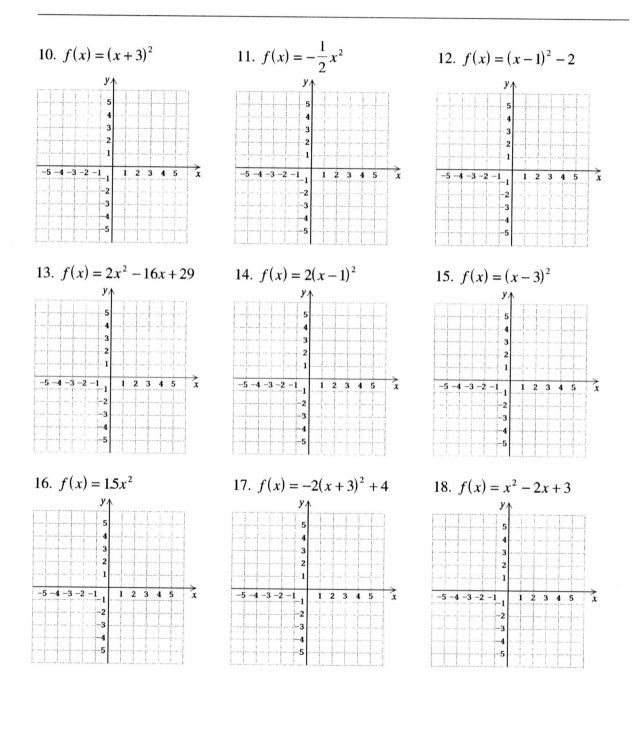

EXTRA PRACTICE 26 (continued)
Graphs of Quadratic Functions
Use after Sections 8.6 and 8.7

19. $f(x) = (x+1)^2$

20. $f(x) = (x+2)^2 - 3$

21. $f(x) = -4x^2 + 24x - 35$

22. $f(x) = -\dfrac{1}{2}(x+1)^2 + 4$

23. $f(x) = -2(x-1)^2$

24. $f(x) = -4x^2$

25. $f(x) = x^2 + 6x + 7$

26. $f(x) = -(x+4)^2$

27. $f(x) = 4x^2 - 4x + 1$

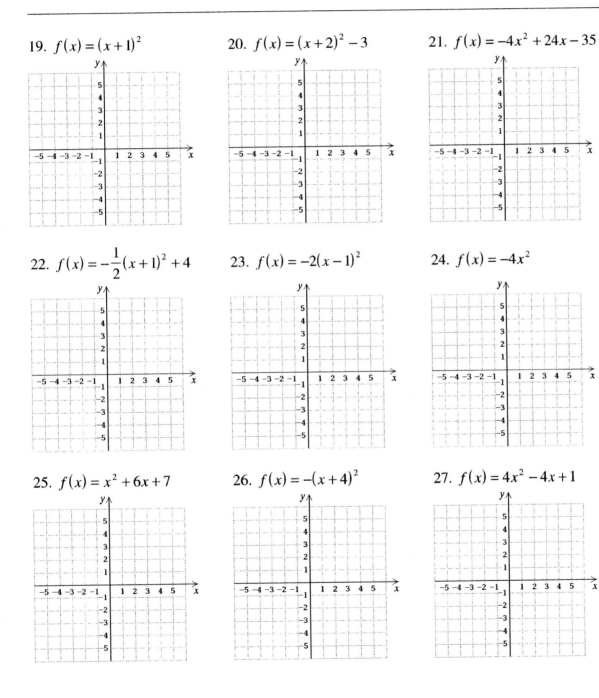

EXTRA PRACTICE 26 (continued)
Graphs of Quadratic Functions
Use after Sections 8.6 and 8.7

28. $f(x) = \dfrac{1}{3}(x+3)^2$

29. $f(x) = -x^2 - 4x - 9$

30. $f(x) = 2x^2 - 4x - 3$

31. $f(x) = (x+2)^2 - 1$

32. $f(x) = -4(x-1)^2 + 1$

33. $f(x) = \dfrac{1}{4}(x-4)^2$

34. $f(x) = -\dfrac{1}{2}(x+2)^2$

35. $f(x) = x^2 - x + 1$

36. $f(x) = -3x^2 - 6x - 1$

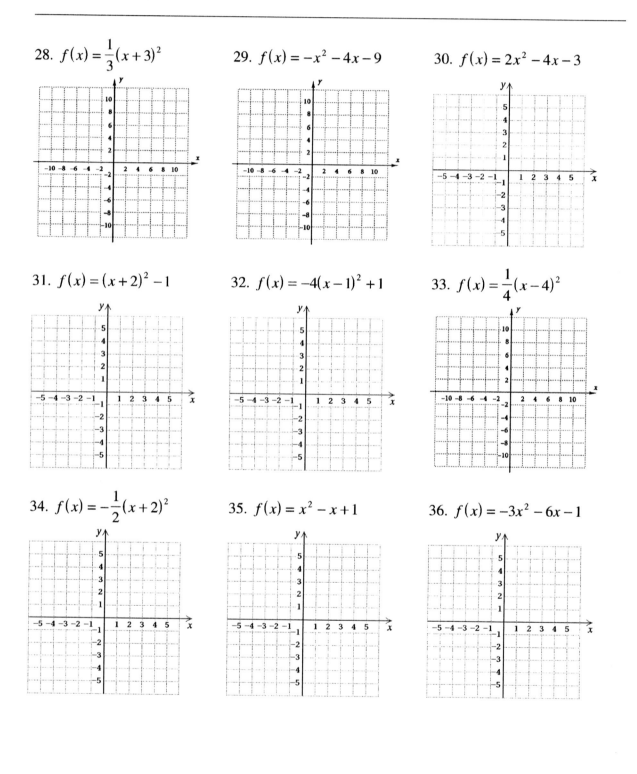

EXTRA PRACTICE 27
More Graphs of Quadratic Functions
Use after Section 8.7   Name_____

Example: Graph $f(x) = x^2 - 2x - 3$.

The *y*-intercept is found by finding $f(0)$. In $f(x) = x^2 - 2x - 3$, the *y*-intercept is $(0,-3)$.

The *x*-intercept(s) are found when $f(x) = 0$. Solve $x^2 - 2x - 3 = 0$ either by factoring or using the quadratic formula.

$$x^2 - 2x - 3 = 0$$
$$(x - 3)(x + 1) = 0$$
$$x = 3 \text{ or } x = -1$$

The *x*-intercepts are $(3,0)$ and $(-1,0)$.

The *x*-coordinate of the vertex is found by using $-\dfrac{b}{2a}$ from the quadratic equation

$f(x) = ax^2 + bx + c$. The second coordinate of the vertex is found by substituting $-\dfrac{b}{2a}$ for *x*

and computing $f\left(-\dfrac{b}{2a}\right)$. In $f(x) = x^2 - 2x - 3$, $a = 1$ and $b = -2$.

The *x*-coordinate of the vertex is $-\dfrac{b}{2a} = -\dfrac{(-2)}{2(1)} = \dfrac{2}{2} = 1$

We substitute 1 for *x* to find the second coordinate of the vertex:

$$f(x) = x^2 - 2x - 3 = (1)^2 - 2(1) - 3 = -4.$$

The vertex is $(1,-4)$. The axis of symmetry is $x = 1$.

We can also look at other points on the parabola and then draw a smooth graph.

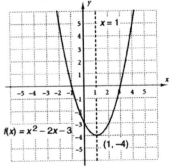

x	y $f(x) = x^2 - 2x - 3$	$(x, f(x))$
-2	5	$(-2,5)$
-1	0	$(-1,0)$
0	-3	$(0,-3)$
1	-4	$(1,-4)$
2	-3	$(2,-3)$

EXTRA PRACTICE 27 (continued)
More Graphs of Quadratic Functions
Use after Section 8.7

Graph the quadratic function. Find the vertex, the line of symmetry, and the maximum or minimum value.

1. $f(x) = 4x^2$

2. $f(x) = x^2 + 3$

3. $f(x) = -x^2 + 4x$

4. $f(x) = x^2 - x - 2$

5. $f(x) = x^2 + 4x + 4$

6. $f(x) = -\dfrac{1}{3}x^2$

7. $f(x) = -x^2 + 2x + 3$

8. $f(x) = 1.5x^2$

9. $f(x) = 4 - x^2$

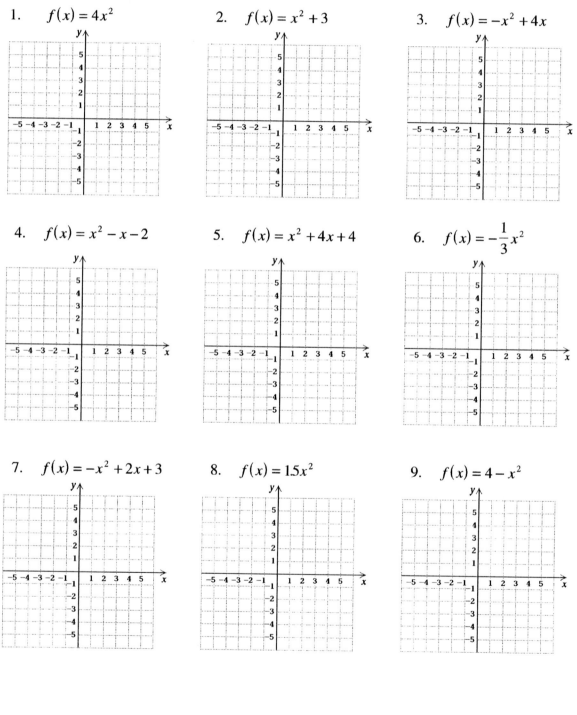

EXTRA PRACTICE 28
Graphing Exponential and Logarithmic Functions
Use after Sections 9.2 and 9.3   Name_____

See Sections 8.1 and 8.3 for examples.

Graph.

1. $f(x) = 2^{x-1}$

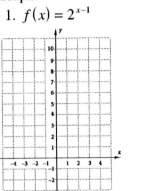

2. $f(x) = 3^x + 2$

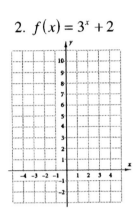

3. $f(x) = 2^x - 4$

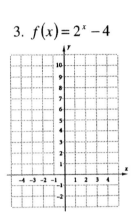

4. $f(x) = 5^{x-3}$

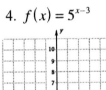
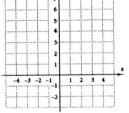

5. $f(x) = 4^{x+1}$

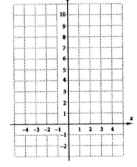

6. $f(x) = 2^x + 1$

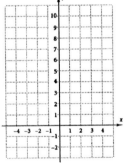

7. $f(x) = \left(\dfrac{1}{2}\right)^x$

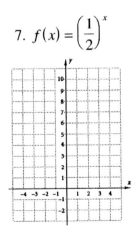

8. $f(x) = 4^{2-x}$

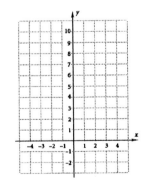

9. $f(x) = 2^{3x-1}$

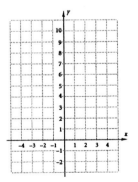
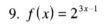

EXTRA PRACTICE 28 (continued)
Graphing Exponential and Logarithmic Functions
Use after Sections 9.2 and 9.3

10. $x = 3^y$ 11. $x = \left(\dfrac{1}{3}\right)^y$ 12. $x = \left(\dfrac{3}{4}\right)^y$

13. $f(x) = \log_3 x$ 14. $f(x) = \log_5 x$ 15. $f(x) = \log_{1/2} x$

16. $f(x) = \log_{1/4} x$ 17. $f(x) = \log_2 x$ 18. $f(x) = \log_{1/3} x$

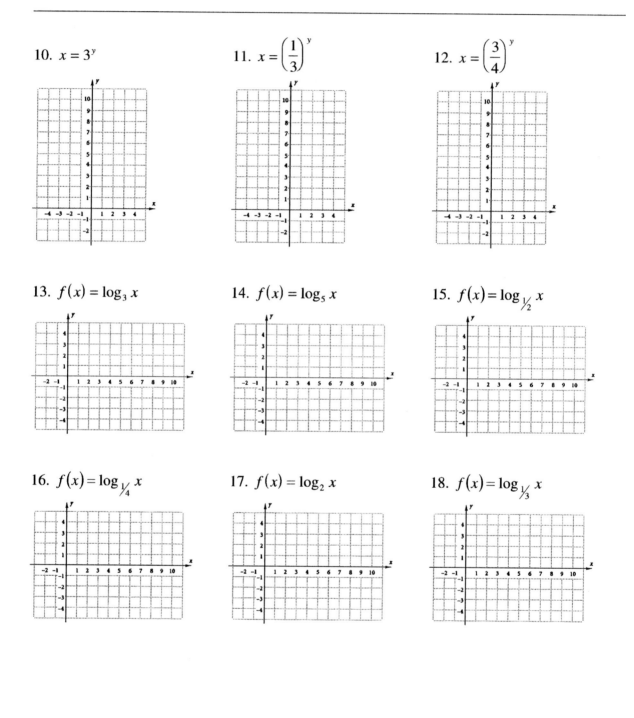

EXTRA PRACTICE 29
Solving Exponential and Logarithmic Equations
Use after Section 9.6   Name_____

Examples. Solve.

a) $7^{x-1} = 343$
    $7^{x-1} = 7^3$
    $x - 1 = 3$

    $x = 4$

b) $6^x = 15$
    $\log 6^x = \log 15$
    $x \log 6 = \log 15$
    $x = \dfrac{\log 15}{\log 6}$
    $x \approx \dfrac{1.1761}{0.7782}$
    $x \approx 1.5113$

c) $e^{-3t} = 0.04$
    $\ln e^{-3t} = \ln 0.04$
    $-3t \ln e = \ln 0.04$
    $-3t = \ln 0.04$
    $t = \dfrac{\ln 0.04}{-3}$
    $t \approx \dfrac{-3.2189}{-3}$
    $t \approx 1.073$

Solve.

1. $3^{5x} = 81$ _____

2. $e^{4t} = 120$ _____

3. $4^x = 6$ _____

4. $6^x = 2$ _____

5. $e^{-2t} = 0.6$ _____

6. $5^{3x+2} = 625$ _____

7. $8^{x+1} = 16$ _____

8. $10^x = 7$ _____

9. $7^x = 1520$ _____

10. $e^{0.04t} = 10$ _____

11. $e^{5t} = 5$ _____

12. $6^x = 7.1$ _____

13. $6^{x+3} = 36$ _____

14. $4^{x-1} = 3$ _____

15. $12^{2x-3} = 16$ _____

16. $10^{5-x} = 1000$ _____

EXTRA PRACTICE 29 (continued)
Solving Exponential and Logarithmic Equations
Use after Section 9.6

Example. Solve: $\log_2(x+1) - \log_2(x-1) = 4$

$\log_2(x+1) - \log_2(x-1) = 4$

$$\log_2 \frac{x+1}{x-1} = 4$$

$$\frac{x+1}{x-1} = 16$$

$$x+1 = 16x - 16$$

$$17 = 15x$$

$$\frac{17}{15} = x$$

The solution is $\dfrac{17}{15}$.

Solve.

Check:

$\log_2(x+1) - \log_2(x-1) = 4$

$$\log_2\left(\frac{17}{15}+1\right) - \log_2\left(\frac{17}{15}-1\right) \;\Big|\; 4$$

$$\log_2 \frac{32}{15} - \log_2 \frac{2}{15}$$

$$\log_2\left(\frac{32}{15} \div \frac{2}{15}\right)$$

$$\log_2 16$$

$$4$$

17. $\log x + \log (x+15) = 2$

18. $\log (x+2) - \log x = 3$

19. $\log_3(2x-7) = 4$

20. $\log_5(x-11) = 2$

21. $\log x + \log (x-21) = 2$

22. $\log_2(x-2) + \log_2(x+2) = 5$

23. $\log (3x+4) = 1$

24. $\log (x+33) - \log x = 2$

25. $\log x - \log (x+5) = -1$

26. $\log_4(x+3) - \log_4 x = 3$

27. $\log_4(x-6) + \log_4(x+6) = 3$

28. $\log_6 x + \log_6(x-9) = 2$

29. $\log x + \log (x-0.21) = -2$

30. $\log (x-48) + \log x = 2$

31. $\log_7 x + \log_7(4x+21) = 3$

32. $\log_2(5-x) = 4$

EXTRA PRACTICE EXERCISES ANSWERS

Extra Practice 1

<u>1</u>. -9 <u>2</u>. -1 <u>3</u>. 5 <u>4</u>. 0 <u>5</u>. -28 <u>6</u>. -12 <u>7</u>. 9 <u>8</u>. -2 <u>9</u>. 15 <u>10</u>. -28 <u>11</u>. -7
<u>12</u>. -1 <u>13</u>. -4 <u>14</u>. -8 <u>15</u>. 3 <u>16</u>. -11 <u>17</u>. 12 <u>18</u>. 7 <u>19</u>. 13 <u>20</u>. 1 <u>21</u>. -12

<u>22</u>. 5 <u>23</u>. 7 <u>24</u>. -7 <u>25</u>. 0 <u>26</u>. -6 <u>27</u>. -2 <u>28</u>. -16 <u>29</u>. $-\dfrac{23}{20}$ <u>30</u>. $\dfrac{1}{8}$ <u>31</u>. $\dfrac{1}{4}$

<u>32</u>. $-\dfrac{8}{15}$ <u>33</u>. $\dfrac{19}{36}$ <u>34</u>. $\dfrac{3}{14}$ <u>35</u>. -5.2 <u>36</u>. 6.5 <u>37</u>. -9.9 <u>38</u>. -3.6 <u>39</u>. 1.6

<u>40</u>. -16.4 <u>41</u>. -16 <u>42</u>. 0 <u>43</u>. 18 <u>44</u>. -5 <u>45</u>. -21 <u>46</u>. 7 <u>47</u>. -5 <u>48</u>. -10
<u>49</u>. 1 <u>50</u>. 14 <u>51</u>. -3 <u>52</u>. -10 <u>53</u>. 11 <u>54</u>. -13 <u>55</u>. -9 <u>56</u>. 12 <u>57</u>. -19 <u>58</u>. 13
<u>59</u>. -2 <u>60</u>. -5 <u>61</u>. 11 <u>62</u>. -8 <u>63</u>. -12 <u>64</u>. 14 <u>65</u>. -8 <u>66</u>. -4 <u>67</u>. 23 <u>68</u>. 6

<u>69</u>. $\dfrac{1}{8}$ <u>70</u>. $-\dfrac{17}{12}$ <u>71</u>. $-\dfrac{3}{20}$ <u>72</u>. $-\dfrac{11}{30}$ <u>73</u>. $\dfrac{59}{60}$ <u>74</u>. $\dfrac{5}{18}$ <u>75</u>. 21 <u>76</u>. -20.4 <u>77</u>. -3.7

<u>78</u>. -2.7 <u>79</u>. -7.1 <u>80</u>. 10.3

Extra Practice 2

<u>1</u>. a) 1 b) -11 c) 5 d) 7.4 e) $\dfrac{13}{2}$ <u>2</u>. a) -5 b) 44 c) 76 d) -3.04 e) $-\dfrac{41}{9}$

<u>3</u>. a) -22 b) -22 c) -22 d) -22 e) -22 <u>4</u>. a) 11 b) -7 c) -8 d) 10
e) 92 <u>5</u>. a) 5 b) 7 c) 32 d) 398 e) $|a-1|$ <u>6</u> a) 0 b) 124 c) -51 d) $128a^3 - 4a$
e) -1990

Extra Practice 3

<u>1</u>. domain $= \{-3,-2,-1,0,1,2\}$; range $= \{4,3,2,1\}$ <u>2</u>. domain $= \{x|-2 \le x \le 1\}$; range $= \{3\}$
<u>3</u>. domain $= \{x|-5 \le x \le 1\}$; range $= \{y|-2 \le y \le 4\}$ <u>4</u>. domain $= \{x|-1 \le x \le 4\}$;
range $= \{y|-3 \le y \le 6\}$ <u>5</u>. domain $= \{x|-2 \le x \le 2\}$; range $= \{y|-4 \le y \le 2\}$
<u>6</u>. domain $= \{x|-5 \le x \le 2\}$; range $= \{y|-2 \le y \le 3\}$ <u>7</u>. x is a real number and $x \ne 2$;
or $(-\infty,2) \cup (2,\infty)$ <u>8</u>. All real numbers   <u>9</u>. All real numbers   <u>10</u>. x is a real number and
$x \ne \dfrac{5}{6}$; or $\left(-\infty,\dfrac{5}{6}\right) \cup \left(\dfrac{5}{6},\infty\right)$ <u>11</u>. x is a real number and $x \ne -\dfrac{3}{2}$; or $\left(-\infty,-\dfrac{3}{2}\right) \cup \left(-\dfrac{3}{2},\infty\right)$
<u>12</u>. All real numbers   <u>13</u>. All real numbers   <u>14</u>. x is a real number and $x \ne -3$; or
$(-\infty,-3) \cup (-3,\infty)$ <u>15</u>. All real numbers

Extra Practice 4

<u>1</u>. 8   <u>2</u>. -30 <u>3</u>. $w = 9$ cm; $l = 17$ cm   <u>4</u>. $w = 16$ m; $l = 23$ m   <u>5</u>. 49, 50, 51
<u>6</u>. 85, 87, 89   <u>7</u>. 2 ft; 6 ft; 12 ft   <u>8</u>. 50 m; 100 m; 300 m   <u>9</u>. 20°, 60°, 100°   <u>10</u>. 46°; 92°;
42°   <u>11</u>. 1000 mi   <u>12</u>. 20

Extra Practice 5

<u>1</u>. 61   <u>2</u>. 194   <u>3</u>. -182 <u>4</u>. 32   <u>5</u>. -87 <u>6</u>. $-\dfrac{4}{3}$ <u>7</u>. $\dfrac{1}{8}$ <u>8</u>. $\dfrac{5}{6}$ <u>9</u>. -4 <u>10</u>. 8

<u>11</u>. $-\dfrac{32}{5}$ <u>12</u>. -144 <u>13</u>. $-\dfrac{8}{15}$ <u>14</u>. 14   <u>15</u>. -18 <u>16</u>. 184   <u>17</u>. 3   <u>18</u>. 118   <u>19</u>. $\dfrac{1}{10}$

<u>20</u>. $-\dfrac{5}{2}$ <u>21</u>. 62   <u>22</u>. -180 <u>23</u>. -1 <u>24</u>. $-\dfrac{2}{3}$ <u>25</u>. $-\dfrac{11}{8}$ <u>26</u>. -55 <u>27</u>. 1   <u>28</u>. 6

<u>29</u>. -16 <u>30</u>. -5 <u>31</u>. 7   <u>32</u>. 6   <u>33</u>. -8 <u>34</u>. -11 <u>35</u>. 3   <u>36</u>. 4   <u>37</u>. 77   <u>38</u>. -9

<u>39</u>. 2   <u>40</u>. -6 <u>41</u>. $\dfrac{5}{2}$ <u>42</u>. -8 <u>43</u>. 1   <u>44</u>. 6   <u>45</u>. 2   <u>46</u>. $-\dfrac{4}{9}$ <u>47</u>. $-\dfrac{15}{2}$ <u>48</u>. -36

<u>49</u>. 75   <u>50</u>. -66 <u>51</u>. 0   <u>52</u>. 0   <u>53</u>. 0   <u>54</u>. 0

Extra Practice 6

<u>1</u>. $r = \dfrac{A - p}{pt}$ <u>2</u>. $t = \dfrac{A - p}{pr}$ <u>3</u>. $l = \dfrac{V}{wh}$ <u>4</u>. $h = \dfrac{V}{lw}$ <u>5</u>. $d_1 = \dfrac{2A}{d_2}$ <u>6</u>. $d_2 = \dfrac{2A}{d_1}$

<u>7</u>. $m = \dfrac{y - b}{x}$ <u>8</u>. $b = y - mx$ <u>9</u>. $a = \dfrac{pt}{100}$ <u>10</u>. $x = \dfrac{yz}{k}$ <u>11</u>. $\pi = \dfrac{A}{2r}$ <u>12</u>. $h = \dfrac{V}{\pi r^2}$

Extra Practice 7

<u>1</u>.

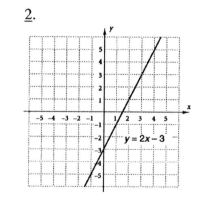

<u>2</u>.

<u>3</u>.

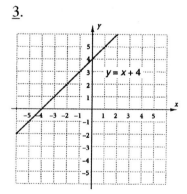

Extra Practice 7 (continued)

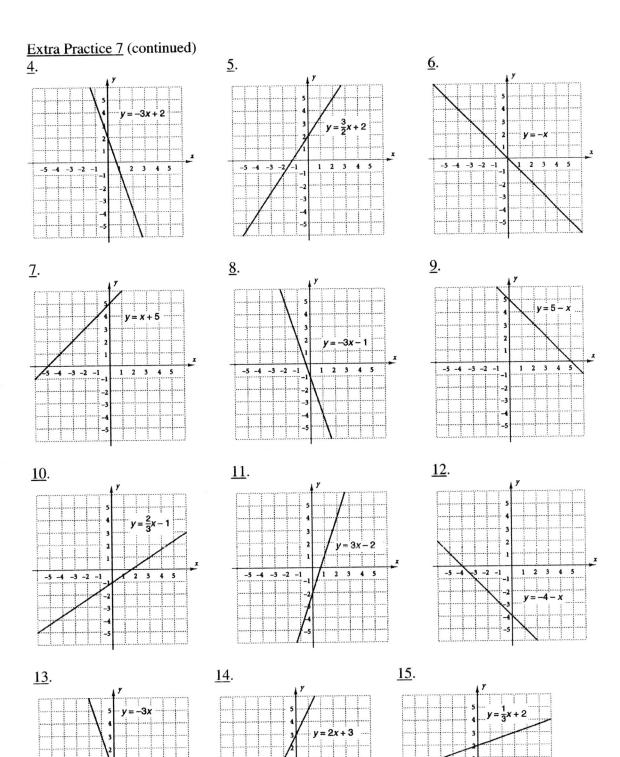

4. $y = -3x + 2$

5. $y = \frac{3}{2}x + 2$

6. $y = -x$

7. $y = x + 5$

8. $y = -3x - 1$

9. $y = 5 - x$

10. $y = \frac{2}{3}x - 1$

11. $y = 3x - 2$

12. $y = -4 - x$

13. $y = -3x$

14. $y = 2x + 3$

15. $y = \frac{1}{3}x + 2$

Extra practice 7 (continued)
16.

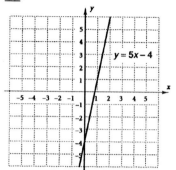

Extra Practice 8

1.

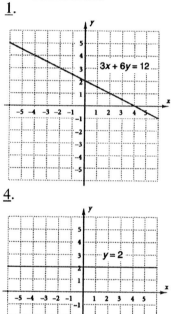

2.

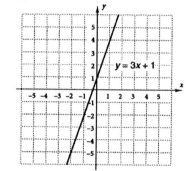

3.

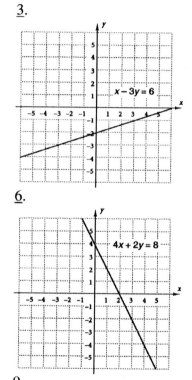

4.

5.

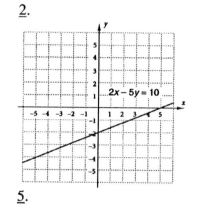

6.

7.

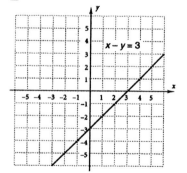

8.

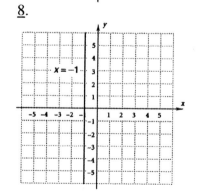

9.

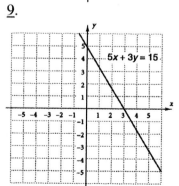

Extra Practice 9

1. $y = -x + 1$ 2. $y = 2x + 4$ 3. $y = 3x + 23$ 4. $y = -2x + 11$ 5. $y = -3x + 16$

6. $y = 2x - 12$ 7. $y = 4x - 28$ 8. $y = -2x + 9$ 9. $y = \frac{1}{5}x - 2$ 10. $y = \frac{1}{4}x - \frac{5}{4}$

11. $y = -x + 6$ 12. $y = -x - 2$ 13. $y = \frac{1}{3}x - \frac{4}{3}$ 14. $y = -\frac{3}{2}x + 3$ 15. $y = -\frac{1}{2}x - 1$

16. $y = \frac{2}{9}x + \frac{2}{3}$ 17. $y = x + 2$ 18. $y = -\frac{4}{3}x$ 19. $y = x + 11$ 20. $y = -6x + 49$

Extra Practice 10

1. $(-2,3)$ 2. $(5,4)$ 3. $(1,3)$ 4. $(5,-1)$ 5. $(-3,4)$ 6. $(2,2)$ 7. $(-1,-3)$ 8. $(4,-5)$
9. $(3,3)$ 10. $(6,-2)$ 11. $(-1,-1)$ 12. $(2,-6)$ 13. $(8,1)$ 14. $(-4,-4)$ 15. $(2,1)$
16. $(-5,3)$ 17. $\left(\frac{11}{3}, -\frac{5}{6}\right)$ 18. $(2,4)$ 19. $\left(\frac{1}{4}, \frac{1}{3}\right)$ 20. $(18,24)$

Extra Practice 11

1. 18, 31   2. 40°, 140°   3. 27°, 63°   4. Length: 59 cm; width: 21 cm   5. 7, −18   6. 21, 35   7. Length: 29 ft; width: 13 ft   8. 39, −18   9. Length: 39 ft; width: 16 ft   10. 25°, 65°

Extra Practice 12

1. $\{y|y > 6\}$ 2. $\{x|x \geq 4\}$ 3. $\{x|x < 7\}$ 4. $\{a|a \geq 2\}$ 5. $\{x|x < 1\}$ 6. $\{y|y < -7\}$

7. $\left\{x|x \geq \frac{11}{5}\right\}$ 8. $\{x|x \leq -2\}$ 9. $\{y|y > 2\}$ 10. $\{t|t \geq -5\}$ 11. $\left\{x|x < \frac{28}{3}\right\}$

12. $\{y|y > 1\}$ 13. $\{y|y \geq 1\}$ 14. $\{m|m \leq 2\}$ 15. $\left\{x|x > \frac{4}{7}\right\}$ 16. $\{x|x \leq -4\}$

17. $\{x|x < 5\}$ 18. $\{x|x > 5\}$ 19. $\{y|y \geq 13\}$ 20. $\{m|m > 3\}$ 21. $\left\{x|x \geq -\frac{1}{12}\right\}$

22. $\{y|y > -4\}$ 23. $\{x|x \leq 3\}$ 24. $\{x|x < 3\}$ 25. $\left\{x|x > \frac{5}{6}\right\}$ 26. $\left\{y|y \leq \frac{1}{6}\right\}$

27. $\{x|x < 4\}$ 28. $\{x|x > -5\}$ 29. $\{y|y < -3\}$ 30. $\{y|y > -4\}$

Extra Practice 13

1. $\left\{x \mid x < -\dfrac{9}{4} \text{ or } x > 3\right\}$ 2. $\left\{y \mid -5 \le y \le 9\right\}$ 3. $\left\{x \mid -\dfrac{31}{5} < x < 3\right\}$ 4. $\{2, 7\}$ 5. $\{-4, 4\}$

6. $\left\{y \mid y \le 0 \text{ or } y \ge 12\right\}$ 7. $\left\{y \mid -11 \le y \le -7\right\}$ 8. $\left\{y \mid y < -\dfrac{5}{3} \text{ or } y > 1\right\}$

9. $\left\{x \mid x < -\dfrac{5}{2} \text{ or } x > 4\right\}$ 10. $\{x \mid -16 < x < 16\}$ 11. $\{-0.34, 0.6\}$

12. $\left\{x \mid x \le -\dfrac{3}{2} \text{ or } x \ge 6\right\}$ 13. $\{x \mid x < -26 \text{ or } x > 8\}$ 14. $\left\{-1, -\dfrac{1}{2}\right\}$

15. $\left\{y \mid y < -2 \text{ or } y > 20\right\}$ 16. $\left\{y \mid -\dfrac{1}{5} \le y \le \dfrac{1}{5}\right\}$ 17. $\left\{y \mid y < -1 \text{ or } y > 1\right\}$ 18. $\{1, 5\}$

19. $\left\{x \mid x \le -\dfrac{13}{5} \text{ or } x \ge \dfrac{17}{5}\right\}$ 20. $\left\{x \mid -\dfrac{3}{2} < x < 10\right\}$ 21. $\{-48, 54\}$

22. $\{x \mid x < 0 \text{ or } x > 38\}$ 23. $\left\{x \mid -\dfrac{1}{4} \le x \le 1\right\}$ 24. $\left\{y \mid -3 < y < 12\right\}$

25. $\left\{y \mid y < -9 \text{ or } y > 9\right\}$ 26. $\left\{y \mid \dfrac{1}{27} \le y \le \dfrac{1}{3}\right\}$ 27. $\left\{y \mid -9 < y < \dfrac{43}{3}\right\}$

28. $\{x \mid x \le -7 \text{ or } x \ge 2\}$ 29. $\left\{x \mid x \le -\dfrac{2}{9} \text{ or } x \ge \dfrac{2}{3}\right\}$ 30. $\left\{y \mid 5 \le y \le 12\right\}$

Extra Practice 14

1. $(x - 8)(x + 2)$ 2. $(4y - 1)(y + 2)$ 3. $5a(a^2 - 5a + 3)$ 4. $(3x + 4)(3x - 4)$

5. $(x + 8)(x - 8)$ 6. $(a + 9)(a + 3)$ 7. $6(x + 1)^2$ 8. $(x^2 - 5)(x + 2)$ 9. $(x - 7)(x - 3)$

10. $3x^2(4x^3 - 2x + 1)$ 11. $6(y + 3)(y - 3)$ 12. $(4y + 3)(y - 5)$ 13. $(2x - 1)(3x - 2)$

14. $5(x - 1)(x + 1)$ 15. $(y^2 + 3)(y^3 + 4)$ 16. $(x - 9)(x + 2)$ 17. $(x - 4)^2$

18. $(a - 7)(a - 2)$ 19. $(7x + 1)(7x - 1)$ 20. $4x^2(2x^2 - x + 3)$ 21. $(y + 5)^2$

22. $3(a^2 + 4a - 1)$ 23. $(x^2 + 9)(x + 3)(x - 3)$ 24. $(3y - 2)^2$ 25. $(a + 5)(a + 6)$

26. $(4t + 3)(2t - 1)$ 27. $3(5x - 1)^2$ 28. $(3t + 1)(t - 3)$ 29. $(x + 8)(x + 3)$ 30. $(y - 11)^2$

31. $(x - 3)(x + 1)$ 32. $4(x - 3)^2$ 33. $(y - 5)(y - 1)$ 34. $(5t + 2)(5t - 2)$

35. $7x(2x^2 - x + 3)$ 36. $(3x + 7)^2$ 37. $9(x + 3)(x - 3)$ 38. $(6x + 5)(2x - 1)$

39. $(7a - 2)^2$ 40. $(8x + 3)(x - 4)$

Extra Practice 15

1. 2   2. $\dfrac{2(x^2+3x+10)}{(x-2)(x+6)}$ 3. $a+4$ 4. $\dfrac{-y^2+7y}{(y-2)(y+1)(y+3)}$ 5. $\dfrac{2x-3}{x-1}$

6. $\dfrac{2a-13}{(a-2)(a+2)}$ 7. $\dfrac{-y-13}{6(y+3)}$ 8. $\dfrac{2}{a}$ 9. $\dfrac{x+7}{(x-5)(x+1)}$ 10. $\dfrac{2}{b+3}$ 11. $\dfrac{2a-5}{a(a-5)}$

12. $\dfrac{4(y+2)}{(y-7)(y+7)}$ 13. $\dfrac{3x+1}{x(x+1)}$ 14. $\dfrac{3b-4}{6b}$ 15. $\dfrac{4x-3}{x+2}$ 16. $\dfrac{x-20}{x(x-4)(x+3)}$

17. $\dfrac{2a^2-4a-5}{(a-1)(a+1)}$ 18. $\dfrac{x+3}{x-5}$ 19. $\dfrac{-23y-11}{6y}$ 20. $\dfrac{3x(x-6)}{(x-9)(x+9)}$

Extra Practice 16

1. $\dfrac{13}{3}$ 2. $-\dfrac{52}{9}$ 3. $\dfrac{1+4x}{1-2x}$ 4. $\dfrac{16+4a^2}{5a^2}$ 5. $\dfrac{1-x}{1-2x}$ 6. $\dfrac{11}{4y^2}$ 7. $\dfrac{x}{x+1}$ 8. $\dfrac{4x-1}{4}$

9. $\dfrac{a-b}{a}$ 10. $\dfrac{1}{x-y}$ 11. $\dfrac{4m^2+3}{2m-5m^2}$ 12. $\dfrac{3-2x^2}{6x^2+5}$ 13. $-\dfrac{1}{y}$ 14. $\dfrac{3x^2-2}{x^3}$ 15. $\dfrac{1}{2a}$

16. $\dfrac{4y^2+3xy}{2x+y^2}$

Extra Practice 17

1. 5   2. 23   3. 2   4. -5 5. 5   6. $-\dfrac{25}{3}$ 7. -7 8. 9   9. $\dfrac{3}{4}$ 10. $-1, 3$ 11. 8

12. $-\dfrac{10}{7}$ 13. 1, 5   14. $-7, \dfrac{3}{2}$ 15. $-\dfrac{1}{2}, 6$ 16. $-\dfrac{1}{13}, 1$ 17. 4   18. -7

Extra Practice 18

1. $-1, 3$ 2. 1, 2   3. $\dfrac{12}{7}$ hours   4. $\dfrac{120}{13}$ hours   5. 50 km/h, 80 km/h   6. Freight: 84 mph; Passenger: 100 mph   7. 585 km   8. 620   9. 9.6   10. 10   11. 2075

Extra Practice 19

1. $4x^4-\dfrac{1}{2}x^2$ 2. $\dfrac{1}{2}x^5+5x^3+3x$ 3. $1-4y+y^3$ 4. $27x^6-15x^2+3$

5. $-5x^5+4x^2-3$ 6. $4y^3+3y^2-2y$ 7. $-4rs-5s^2+3r$ 8. $xy-3+5xy^3$ 9. $x+7$

10. $x-8$ 11. $x-9$ 12. $x+11$ 13. $x+12+\dfrac{75}{x-5}$ 14. $x+15+\dfrac{27}{x-3}$

Extra Practice 19 (continued)

15. $2x^2 - 3x + 5$ 16. $4x^2 - 9$ 17. $x^3 + x^2 - x - 1 + \dfrac{2}{x-1}$ 18. $x^3 - 2x^2 + 9x - 18 + \dfrac{38}{x+2}$

19. $x^3 - 9$ 20. $x^3 + 4 + \dfrac{-2}{x^3 - 2}$ 21. $x^3 - 3x^2 + 9x - 27$ 22. $x^2 + 4x + 16$ 23. $a^2 + 25$

24. $a^2 - 10a + 75 + \dfrac{-500}{a+5}$

Extra Practice 20

1. $2xz\sqrt{5xy}$ 2. $4x\sqrt[3]{2xy^2}$ 3. a^4b^3 4. $\dfrac{7a\sqrt{a}}{b^2}$ 5. $3ac\sqrt{5ab}$ 6. 64 7. $\dfrac{2x\sqrt[3]{2x^2}}{y^2}$

8. $2ab^3\sqrt[4]{4a^3}$ 9. $5ab^2\sqrt{2b}$ 10. $8x^6$ 11. $\dfrac{4x\sqrt{x}}{9}$ 12. $10xz^5\sqrt{5yz}$ 13. 36 14. $\dfrac{4a^2\sqrt[3]{a}}{3}$

15. $2xy\sqrt[3]{30xy^2}$ 16. $xy^2z^3\sqrt[4]{x^3y}$ 17. $\dfrac{2x\sqrt{6x}}{5}$ 18. 64 19. $8a^3b^6$ 20. $9a^2\sqrt[3]{4}$

21. $5(x+2)\sqrt[3]{x+2}$ 22. $4a^2\sqrt{b}$ 23. $6x$ 24. $4x^2\sqrt[3]{x^2y^2}$ 25. $2x^2y\sqrt{6y}$ 26. $3ab^2\sqrt[3]{a}$

27. $5xy\sqrt[3]{x^2}$ 28. $3(x+3)^2\sqrt{2}$ 29. $36a\sqrt[3]{6b^2}$ 30. $3y^2$ 31. $6xy\sqrt[5]{x^2y^4}$

32. $2(y-3)^2\sqrt[3]{y-3}$

Extra Practice 21

1. $\dfrac{\sqrt{42}}{7}$ 2. $\dfrac{\sqrt{10}}{5}$ 3. $\dfrac{2\sqrt{6xy}}{3y}$ 4. $\dfrac{\sqrt{6xy}}{3y}$ 5. $\dfrac{\sqrt[3]{75x^2y^2}}{5y^2}$ 6. $\dfrac{\sqrt[4]{14x^3y^3}}{2x^2}$ 7. $\dfrac{\sqrt[3]{100x^2y^2}}{5y}$

8. $\dfrac{\sqrt[5]{162x^3y^4}}{3y}$ 9. $\dfrac{\sqrt[3]{3xy^2}}{y}$ 10. $\dfrac{\sqrt{15xy}}{3x}$ 11. $\dfrac{2x\sqrt{5y}}{5y}$ 12. $\dfrac{3x^2\sqrt[3]{4y^2}}{2y}$ 13. $\dfrac{4(8+\sqrt{5})}{59}$

14. $-\sqrt{30} - \sqrt{15}$ 15. $\dfrac{9(3+\sqrt{21})}{-2}$, or $\dfrac{27+9\sqrt{21}}{-2}$ 16. $\dfrac{6\sqrt{x}+2\sqrt{6x}}{x}$ 17. $\dfrac{1-\sqrt{21}}{4}$

18. $\dfrac{2x - 3\sqrt{xy} + y}{x-y}$ 19. $\dfrac{7 - 3\sqrt{7x} + 2x}{7-x}$ 20. $\dfrac{2x + 5\sqrt{xy} - 3y}{x-9y}$

Extra Practice 22

1. $1, 2$ 2. 36 3. 7 4. 7 5. $0, 1$ 6. $-3, 0$ 7. 9 8. 30 9. 28 10. 6 11. No solution
12. $-4, 0$ 13. 29 14. 16 15. 6 16. 0 17. No solution   18. 2 19. 8 20. -3

Extra Practice 23

1. $-1, 4$ 2. $2, 4$ 3. 5 4. $-\dfrac{3}{2}, 5$ 5. $-6, 6$ 6. $-7, 7$ 7. $\dfrac{3\pm\sqrt{21}}{2}$ 8. $\dfrac{5\pm\sqrt{53}}{2}$

9. $4\pm\sqrt{5}$ 10. $\dfrac{-7\pm\sqrt{53}}{2}$ 11. $-3\pm\sqrt{5}$ 12. $\dfrac{3\pm\sqrt{29}}{2}$ 13. $\dfrac{-7\pm\sqrt{17}}{8}$ 14. $\dfrac{3\pm\sqrt{29}}{10}$

15. $\dfrac{3\pm\sqrt{33}}{4}$ 16. $\dfrac{-3\pm\sqrt{57}}{6}$ 17. $\dfrac{3\pm\sqrt{13}}{4}$ 18. $1, \dfrac{3}{2}$ 19. $-5, 5$ 20. $-4, 4$

Extra Practice 24

1. $11\sqrt{2}$ cm   2. 15 cm   3. 7 in. x 12 in.   4. 30 m   5. $l = 15$ in.; $w = 60$ in.   6. 8 ft, 15 ft
7. 17 in.   8. 10 in.   9. 2.4 in.   10. 4 ft   11. About 8.1 mph   12. 5 km/h

Extra Practice 25

1. 81   2. $\pm\sqrt{2}, \pm\sqrt{6}$ 3. $-\dfrac{1}{3}, \dfrac{1}{4}$ 4. $-\dfrac{4}{3}, \dfrac{4}{3}$ 5. 1, 81   6. 4, 169   7. $\pm\sqrt{2}, \pm 2$

8. 16, 81   9. $-2, -1, 3, 4$ 10. $\pm\sqrt{3}, \pm i\sqrt{7}$ 11. $-1, 1, 4, 6$ 12. 4, 100   13. $\dfrac{3}{4}$

14. 144, 225   15. $\pm\sqrt{3}, \pm 2$ 16. $-\dfrac{1}{5}, \dfrac{2}{3}$

Extra Practice 26

1.

2.

3.

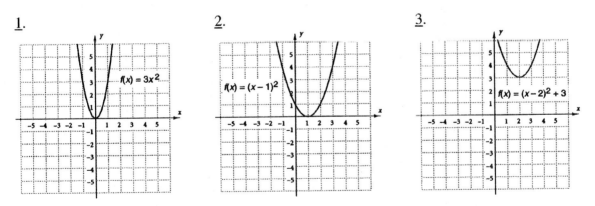

Extra Practice 26 (continued)

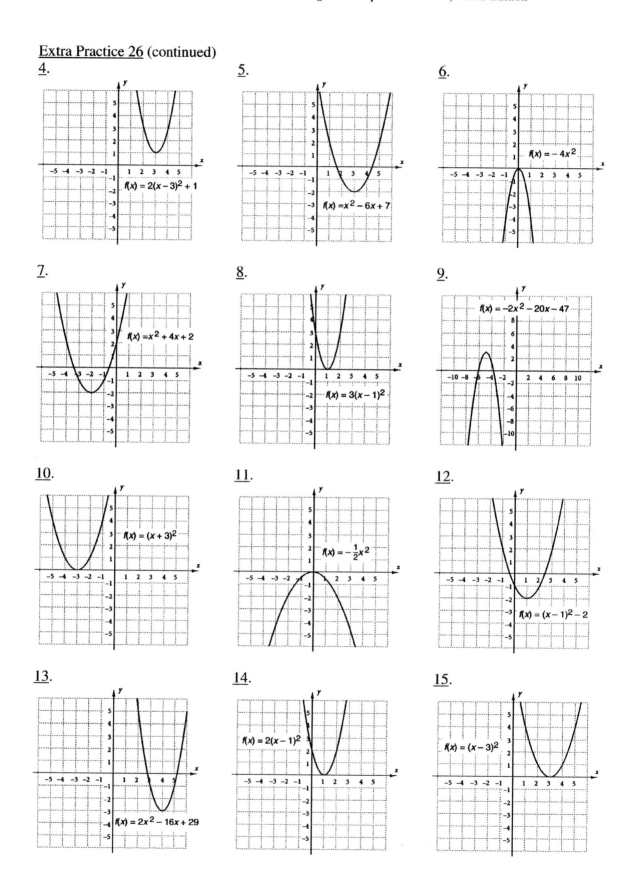

4.

$f(x) = 2(x - 3)^2 + 1$

5.

$f(x) = x^2 - 6x + 7$

6.

$f(x) = -4x^2$

7.

$f(x) = x^2 + 4x + 2$

8.

$f(x) = 3(x - 1)^2$

9.

$f(x) = -2x^2 - 20x - 47$

10.

$f(x) = (x + 3)^2$

11.

$f(x) = -\frac{1}{2}x^2$

12.

$f(x) = (x - 1)^2 - 2$

13.

$f(x) = 2x^2 - 16x + 29$

14.

$f(x) = 2(x - 1)^2$

15.

$f(x) = (x - 3)^2$

Extra Practice 26 (continued)

16.

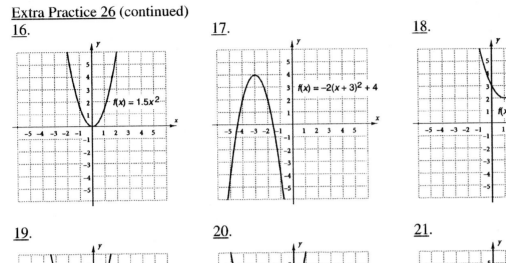

$f(x) = 1.5x^2$

17.

$f(x) = -2(x + 3)^2 + 4$

18.

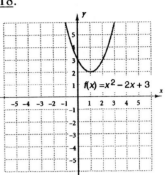

$f(x) = x^2 - 2x + 3$

19.

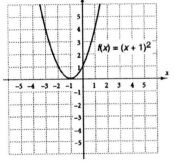

$f(x) = (x + 1)^2$

20.

$f(x) = (x + 2)^2 - 3$

21.

$f(x) = -4x^2 + 24x - 35$

22.

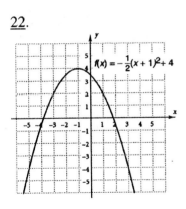

$f(x) = -\frac{1}{2}(x + 1)^2 + 4$

23.

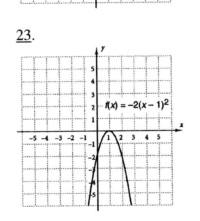

$f(x) = -2(x - 1)^2$

24.

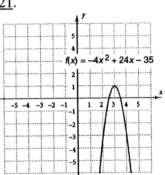

$f(x) = -4x^2$

25.

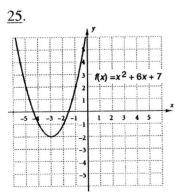

$f(x) = x^2 + 6x + 7$

26.

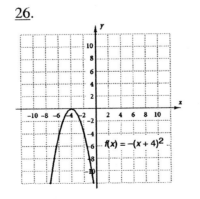

$f(x) = -(x + 4)^2$

27.

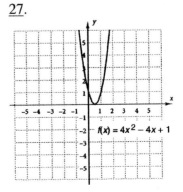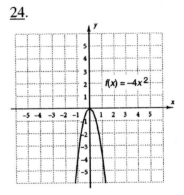

$f(x) = 4x^2 - 4x + 1$

Extra Practice 26 (continued)

<u>28.</u>

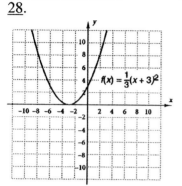

$f(x) = \frac{1}{3}(x + 3)^2$

<u>29.</u>

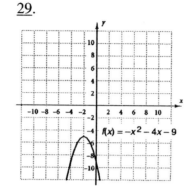

$f(x) = -x^2 - 4x - 9$

<u>30.</u>

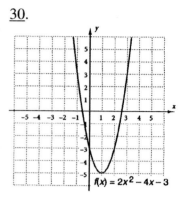

$f(x) = 2x^2 - 4x - 3$

<u>31.</u>

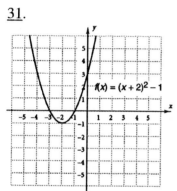

$f(x) = (x + 2)^2 - 1$

<u>32.</u>

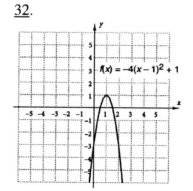

$f(x) = -4(x - 1)^2 + 1$

<u>33.</u>

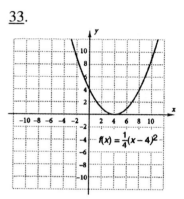

$f(x) = \frac{1}{4}(x - 4)^2$

<u>34.</u>

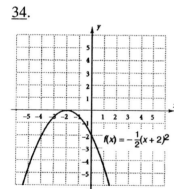

$f(x) = -\frac{1}{2}(x + 2)^2$

<u>35.</u>

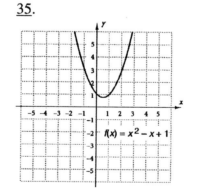

$f(x) = x^2 - x + 1$

<u>36.</u>

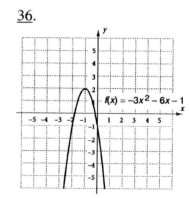

$f(x) = -3x^2 - 6x - 1$

Extra Practice 27

<u>1.</u>

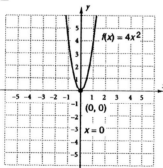

$f(x) = 4x^2$

(0, 0)

$x = 0$

<u>2.</u>

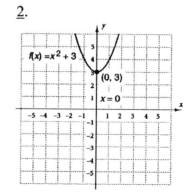

$f(x) = x^2 + 3$

(0, 3)

$x = 0$

<u>3.</u>

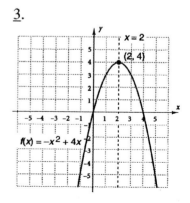

$x = 2$

(2, 4)

$f(x) = -x^2 + 4x$

Extra Practice 27 (continued)

4.

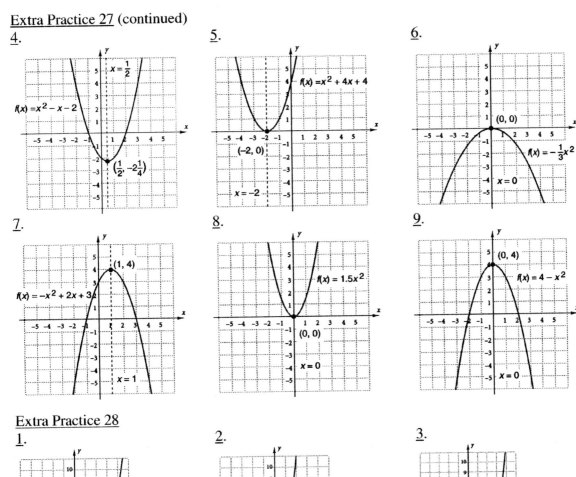

$f(x) = x^2 - x - 2$

$x = \frac{1}{2}$

$\left(\frac{1}{2}, -2\frac{1}{4}\right)$

5.

$f(x) = x^2 + 4x + 4$

$(-2, 0)$

$x = -2$

6.

$(0, 0)$

$f(x) = -\frac{1}{3}x^2$

$x = 0$

7.

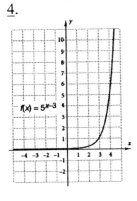

$(1, 4)$

$f(x) = -x^2 + 2x + 3$

$x = 1$

8.

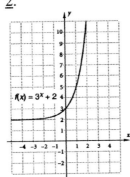

$f(x) = 1.5x^2$

$(0, 0)$

$x = 0$

9.

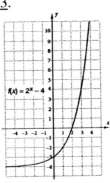

$(0, 4)$

$f(x) = 4 - x^2$

$x = 0$

Extra Practice 28

1.

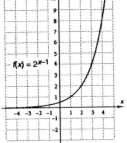

$f(x) = 2^{x-1}$

2.

$f(x) = 3^x + 2$

3.

$f(x) = 2^x - 4$

4.

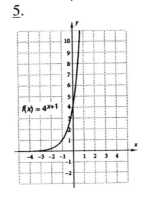

$f(x) = 5^{x-3}$

5.

$f(x) = 4^{x+1}$

6.

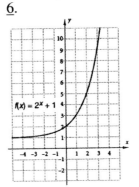

$f(x) = 2^x + 1$

Extra Practice 28 (continued)

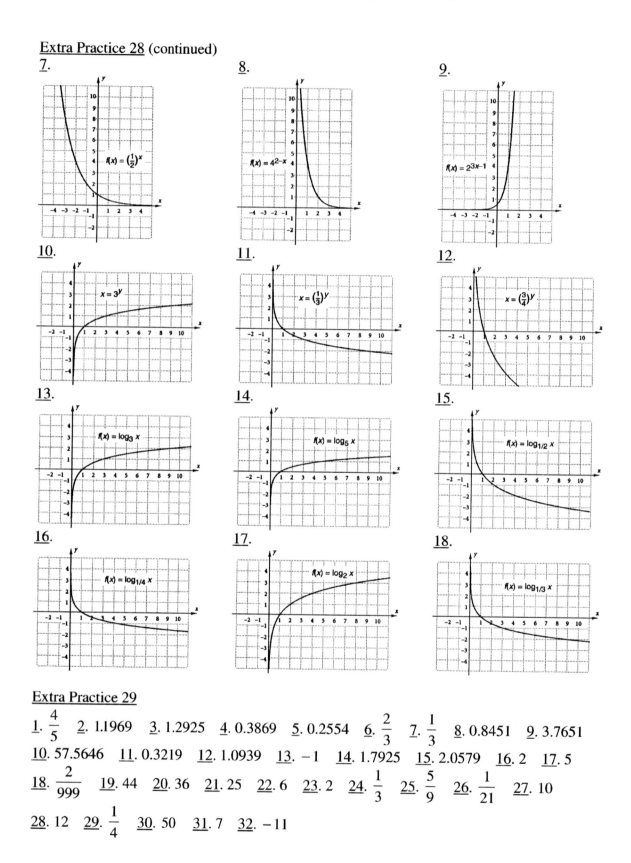

7. $f(x) = \left(\frac{1}{2}\right)^x$

8. $f(x) = 4^{2-x}$

9. $f(x) = 2^{3x-1}$

10. $x = 3^y$

11. $x = \left(\frac{1}{3}\right)^y$

12. $x = \left(\frac{3}{4}\right)^y$

13. $f(x) = \log_3 x$

14. $f(x) = \log_5 x$

15. $f(x) = \log_{1/2} x$

16. $f(x) = \log_{1/4} x$

17. $f(x) = \log_2 x$

18. $f(x) = \log_{1/3} x$

Extra Practice 29

1. $\frac{4}{5}$ 2. 1.1969   3. 1.2925   4. 0.3869   5. 0.2554   6. $\frac{2}{3}$ 7. $\frac{1}{3}$ 8. 0.8451   9. 3.7651

10. 57.5646   11. 0.3219   12. 1.0939   13. −1   14. 1.7925   15. 2.0579   16. 2   17. 5

18. $\frac{2}{999}$ 19. 44   20. 36   21. 25   22. 6   23. 2   24. $\frac{1}{3}$ 25. $\frac{5}{9}$ 26. $\frac{1}{21}$ 27. 10

28. 12   29. $\frac{1}{4}$ 30. 50   31. 7   32. −11

TRANSPARENCY MASTERS

Test Aid: Number Lines

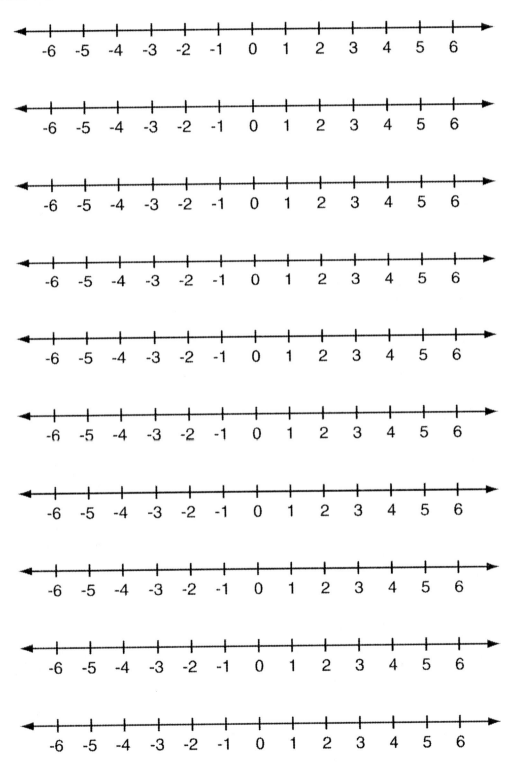

Transparency Master: Number Lines

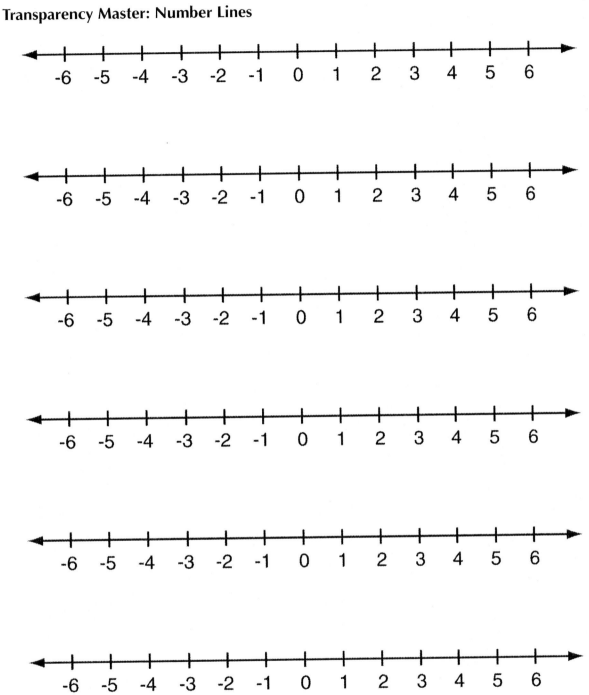

Test Aid: Rectangular Coordinate Grids

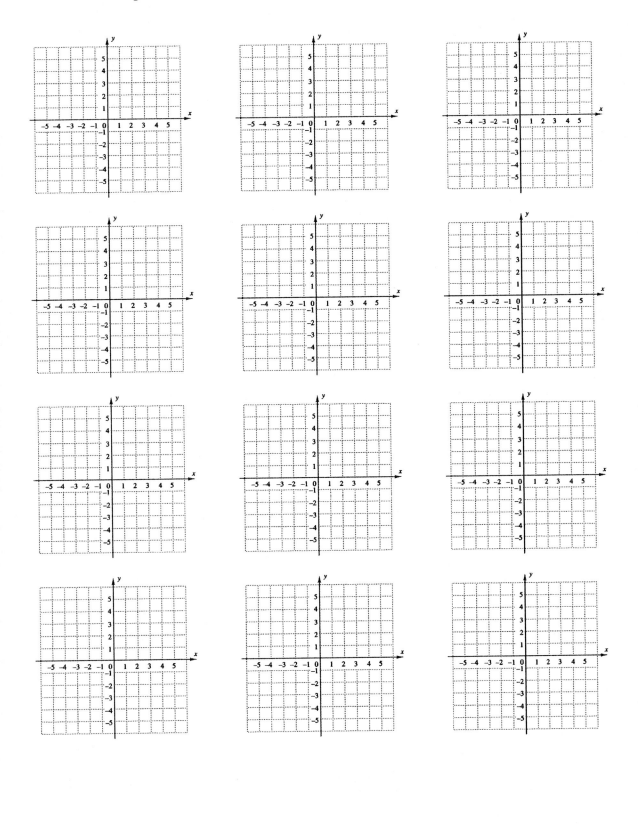

Test Aid: Rectangular Coordinate Grids

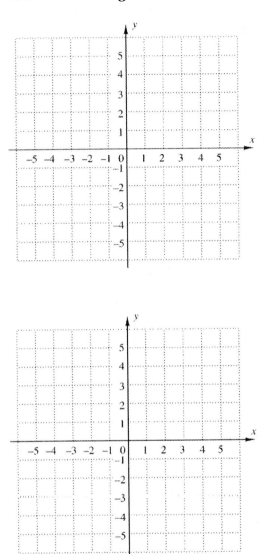

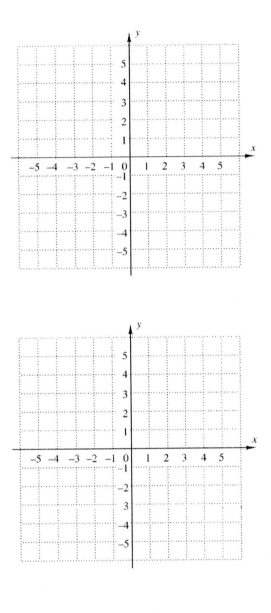

Transparency Master: Rectangular Coordinate Grid

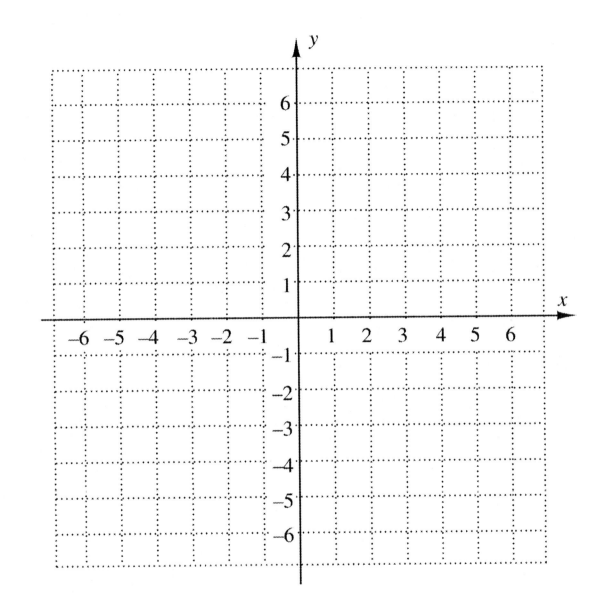

AVAILABLE SUPPLEMENTS

Student Supplements	Instructor Supplements

Student's Solutions Manual
- By James J. Ball and Rhea Meyerholtz, *Indiana State University*
- Contains completely worked-out solutions for all the odd-numbered exercises in the text, with the exception of the Thinking and Writing exercises, as well as completely worked-out solutions to all the exercises in the Chapter Reviews, Chapter Tests, and Cumulative Reviews.
  ISBN-13: 978-0-321-42904-9
  ISBN-10: 0-321-42904-4

Graphing Calculator Manual
- By Judith A. Penna, *Indiana University Purdue University Indianapolis*
- Uses actual examples and exercises from the text to help teach students to use the graphing calculator.
- Order of topics mirrors order in the text, providing a just-in-time mode of instruction.
  ISBN-13: 978-0-321-42612-3
  ISBN-10: 0-321-42612-6

Video Lectures on CD
- Complete set of digitized videos on CD-ROMs for student use at home or on campus.
- Presents a series of lectures correlated directly to the content of each section of the text.
- Features an engaging team of instructors including authors Barbara Johnson and David Ellenbogen who present material in a format that stresses student interaction, often using examples and exercises from the text.
- Ideal for distance learning or supplemental instruction.
- Videos on CD include an expandable window that shows text captioning. Captions can be turned on or off.
  ISBN-13: 978-0-321-42694-9
  ISBN-10: 0-321-42694-0

Annotated Instructor's Edition
- Includes answers to all exercises printed in blue on the same page as those exercises.
  ISBN-13: 978-0-321-42855-4
  ISBN-10: 0-321-42855-2

Instructor's Solutions Manual
- By James J. Ball and Rhea Meyerholtz, *Indiana State University*
- Contains full, worked-out solutions to all the exercises in the exercise sets, including the Thinking and Writing exercises, and worked-out solutions to all the exercises in the Chapter Reviews, Chapter Tests, and Cumulative Reviews.
  ISBN-13: 978-0-321-42534-8
  ISBN-10: 0-321-42534-0

Printed Test Bank
- By Carrie Green
- Provides 8 revised test forms for every chapter and 8 revised test forms for the final exam.
- For the chapter tests, 6 test forms are organized by topic order following the chapter tests in the text, and 2 test forms are multiple-choice.
  ISBN-13: 978-0-321-42680-2
  ISBN-10: 0-321-42680-0

NEW! Instructor and Adjunct Support Manual
- Features resources and teaching tips designed to help both new and adjunct faculty with course preparation and classroom management.
- Resources include extra practice sheets, conversion guide, video index, and transparency masters.
- Also available electronically so course/adjunct coordinators can customize material specific to their schools.
  ISBN-13: 978-0-321-42856-1
  ISBN-10: 0-321-42856-0

Addison-Wesley Math Tutor Center

- The Addison-Wesley Math Tutor Center is staffed by qualified mathematics instructors who provide students with tutoring on examples and odd-numbered exercises from the textbook. Tutoring is available via toll-free telephone, toll-free fax, e-mail, or the Internet. White Board technology allows tutors and students to actually see problems worked while they "talk" in real time over the Internet during tutoring sessions.
www.aw-bc.com/tutorcenter

MathXL® Tutorials on CD

- Provides algorithmically generated practice exercises that correlate at the objective level to the content of the text.
- Includes an example and a guided solution to accompany every exercise and video clips for selected exercises.
- Recognizes student errors and provides feedback; generates printed summaries of students' progress.
ISBN-13: 978-0-321-42783-0
ISBN-10: 0-321-42783-1

TestGen with Quizmaster

- Enables instructors to build, edit, print, and administer tests.
- Features a computerized bank of questions developed to cover all text objectives.
- Algorithmically based content allows instructors to create multiple but equivalent versions of the same question or test with a click of a button.
- Instructors can also modify test-bank questions or add new questions by using the built-in question editor, which allows users to create graphs, input graphics, and insert math notation, variable numbers, or text.
- Tests can be printed or administered online via the Internet or another network. Quizmaster allows students to take tests on a local area network.
- Available on a dual-platform Windows/Macintosh CD-ROM.
ISBN-13: 978-0-321-42157-9
ISBN-10: 0-321-42157-4

MathXL® Online Course

MathXL is a powerful online homework, tutorial, and assessment system that uses algorithmically generated exercises correlated at the objective level to your textbook. Instructors can create and assign online homework and tests and can track students' results in MathXL's flexible online gradebook. Students can retry interactive tutorial exercises as many times as they like, with new values each time, for unlimited practice and mastery. They also receive a personalized study plan based on their test results that links directly to exercises for the objectives they need to study and retest. For more information, see page 146.

MyMathLab™ Online Course

MyMathLab is a complete online course that offers all the features of MathXL plus a complete multimedia eBook, additional course-management features, and access to the Addison-Wesley Tutor Center. Powered by CourseCompass' (Pearson's online teaching and leaning environment) and by MathXL (our online homework, tutorial, and assessment system), MyMathLab makes it easy to deliver all or a portion of your course online. Instructors can easily customize MyMathLab to suit their students' needs and help increase their comprehension and success. For more information, see page 147.

InterAct Math® Tutorial Web site: www.interactmath.com

This open-access Web site provides students with algorithmically generated practice exercises correlated to the textbook for unlimited practice and mastery. Students can go to the Web site, select their textbook, chapter, and section, and retry tutorial exercises for that section as many times as they like with new values each time. Exercises are accompanied by an interactive guided solution that provides helpful feedback for incorrect answers, and students can also view a worked-out sample problem that steps them through an exercise similar to the one they're working on.

Getting Started with MathXL

Overview
MathXL® is a powerful online homework, tutorial, and assessment system tied to Pearson Addison-Wesley and Pearson Prentice Hall textbooks in Mathematics and Statistics. Ideal for use in a lecture, self-paced, or distance-learning course, MathXL diagnoses students' weaknesses and creates a personalized study plan based on their test results. MathXL provides students with unlimited practice using a database of algorithmically-generated exercises correlated to the exercises in their textbook. Each tutorial exercise is accompanied by an interactive guided solution and a sample problem to help students improve their skills independently. Instructors can use MathXL to create online homework assignments, quizzes, and tests that are automatically graded and tracked. Instructors can view and manage all students' homework and test results, study plans, and tutorial work in MathXL's flexible online gradebook.

How to Adopt MathXL
1. **Getting Access**
    If you are interested in using MathXL for one or more of your courses, contact your Addison-Wesley sales representative to request a *MathXL Instructor Access Kit.* (If you are not sure who your sales representative is, go to www.aw-bc.com/replocator.) The access kit provides you with an **instructor access code** for registration.
2. **Registering**
    Registering is an easy process that takes only a few minutes, and you need to register only once, even if you are teaching more than one course with MathXL. Detailed instructions are included in the instructor access kit. As part of the registration process, you select a login name and password that you will use from then on to access your MathXL course. Once you have your instructor access code, go to www.mathxl.com, click the **Register** button, and follow the on-screen instructions to register and log in.
3. **Creating Your MathXL Course**
    Once you've registered, creating your MathXL course is easy! Simply log in at www.mathxl.com, go to the Course Manager, and click "Create or copy a course". You will be asked to select the textbook you are using and enter some very basic information about your course. You can create as many courses as you need, and you can customize course coverage to match your syllabus if you wish.
4. **Ordering Books for Your Students**
    To access your MathXL course, each student needs to register in MathXL using a student access code. The easiest way to supply your students with access codes is to order your textbook packaged with the *MathXL Student Access Kit.* Visit the **Books with MathXL** section of the website at www.mathxl.com for a complete list of package ISBNs.

How to Learn More about MathXL
*   To learn more about MathXL, visit our website at www.mathxl.com, or contact your Addison-Wesley sales representative to schedule a demonstration.
*   For detailed instructions on how to register, log in, and set up your first MathXL course, view or print the *Getting Started with MathXL* instructor guide from the MathXL website at www.mathxl.com.

Getting Started with MyMathLab™

Overview
Powered by CourseCompass™ and MathXL®, MyMathLab is a series of text-specific online courses that accompany Pearson Addison-Wesley and Pearson Prentice Hall textbooks in Mathematics and Statistics. Since 2001, more than 1.3 million students at over 1600 colleges and universities have had more success in Math with MyMathLab's dependable and easy-to-use online homework, guided solutions, multimedia, tests, and eBooks. Pearson's premier, proven service teams provide training and support when you need it. And MyMathLab offers the broadest range of titles available for adoption.

When you adopt the MyMathLab course for your textbook, your students can view the textbook pages in electronic form and link to supplemental multimedia resources—such as animations and video clips—directly from the eBook. MyMathLab provides students with algorithmically-generated tutorial exercises correlated to the exercises in their text, and the system generates individualized study plans based on student test results. MyMathLab's powerful homework and test managers and flexible online gradebook make it easy for instructors to create and manage online assignments that are automatically graded, so they can spend less time grading and more time teaching!

How to Adopt MyMathLab
1. **Getting Access**
   If you are interested in using MyMathLab for one or more of your courses, you will need an instructor access code. You can receive an **instructor access code** in one of two ways:
   - Request a *MyMathLab Instructor Access Kit* from your Addison-Wesley sales representative. To identify your sales representative, go to www.aw-bc.com/replocator.
   - Request an access code online by visiting the **Getting Started** section of the MyMathLab website (under the Tours & Training tab) at www.mymathlab.com.
2. **Registering**
   MyMathLab courses are accessed through an online learning environment called CourseCompass, so to adopt a MyMathLab course, you need to register in CourseCompass. Registering is an easy process that takes only a few minutes, and you need to register only once, even if you are teaching more than one MyMathLab course. As part of the registration process, you select a login name and password that you will use from then on to access your MyMathLab course. Once you have your instructor access code, go to www.coursecompass.com, click the **Register** button for instructors, and follow the on-screen instructions to register and log in.
3. **Creating Your MyMathLab Course**
   Once you've registered in CourseCompass, creating your MyMathLab course is easy! You will simply be asked to select the course materials for your textbook and enter some very basic information about your course. Approximately one business day later (and often after only an hour or two), you will be notified via e-mail that your course is ready, and you will then be able to log in and begin exploring MyMathLab.
4. **Ordering Books for Your Students**
   To access your MyMathLab course, each student needs to register in CourseCompass using a student access code. The easiest way to supply your students with access codes is to order your textbook packaged with the *MyMathLab Student Access Kit*. Visit the **Books Available** section of the website at www.mymathlab.com for a complete list of package ISBNs.

How to Learn More about MyMathLab
- To learn more about MyMathLab, visit our website at www.mymathlab.com, or contact your Addison-Wesley sales representative to schedule a demonstration.
- For detailed instructions on how to register, log in, and set up your first MyMathLab course, view or print the *Getting Started with MyMathLab and CourseCompass* instructor guide from the **Getting Started** section of the MyMathLab website (under the Tours & Training tab) at www.mymathlab.com.

HELPFUL TIPS FOR USING SUPPLEMENTS AND TECHNOLOGY

Kandace Kling, *Portland Community College*

I sign up so that my students have an access code to use MyMathLab.

Tamie D. McCabe, *Redlands Community College*

- **TestGen:** I like using the TestGen program. It allows me to make several test versions at once. It gives a variety of problems. The newest version is more user friendly and allows you to change the directions easily. The program also allows me to important into WebCT to create quizzes.

- **Videos:** We make the videos available to the students in our tutoring center as well as in the library. I have several students that will access these tapes for a different approach to a particular topic or refresher of a topic.

- **Student Solution Manual:** I recommend the students purchase the SSM. I tell them to use it as a resource, especially if they can't get to a tutor or watch a video.

Terry Reeves, *Red Rocks Community College*

- I think the MyMathLab online course management system is excellent, and I'm a fan. The math department at RRCC has used this system exclusively for our online classes only. As far as MyMathLab goes, students have told us that the tracked tutorial exercises are very helpful, as well as the online video lectures. We switched to the online delivery system after trying to offer several math sections in a "self-paced" format. Student success has markedly improved since converting these sections to an online, tutorial-based delivery.

- I do have copies of the MathXL tutorial CDs for some of our algebra classes. These I use to loan out to students struggling in a traditional classroom setting.

Matt B. Roscoe, *The University of Montana*

We teach our course in a lecture/lab style where students spend 3 hours a week in a traditional lecture and 2 hours a week in a tutoring lab. Students are required to complete weekly lab exercises that are meant to complement the weeks' lecture content and usually extend the material in application exercises. We have found that this sort of structure provides an efficient method of delivering the course content (lecture) while still providing one on one practice in a group setting where students can be mentored more individually (lab). We will be piloting MathXL next semester for homework collection.

Karen Walters, *Arapahoe Community College*

- TestGen is great for creating exams and study guides. A nice feature is the ability to create several versions of the same exam. You can also edit questions or write your own.

- I recommend that students use InterAct Math to help them with their homework. This online program presents problems similar to the odd-numbered exercises in the textbook. Students can get help solving a problem or view a similar example. They can also work a problem several times (with new values each time) until they are confident that they know how to solve it.

- If students have missed class or are having a tough time with a particular section, I encourage them to watch the corresponding videotape. Students can watch the videotapes in our mathematics support room or they can check them out overnight from the school library.

USEFUL OUTSIDE RESOURCES FOR TEACHERS

Texts

Raymond Blum, *Mathamusements*, © 1999, Sterling Publishing Co., Inc. 0806997842

Daniel Chazan. *Beyond Formulas in Mathematics and Teaching: Dynamics of the High School Algebra Classroom*, © 2000, Teachers College Press, Columbia University. 0807739189

C. M. Charles. *Essential Elements of Effective Discipline*, © 2002, Allyn & Bacon. 0201729482

Randy Davidson & Ellen Levitov. *Overcoming Math Anxiety*, Second Edition, © 2000, Addison-Wesley. 0321069188

Barbara Gross Davis, *Tools for Teaching*, © 1993, Jossey-Bass Publishers, San Francisco. 1555425682

John Gullbery, *Mathematics from the Birth of Numbers*, © 1997, WW Norton and Co. 039304002X

Adam Hart-Davis, *Amazing Math Puzzles*, © 1998, Sterling Publishing, Co., Inc. 0806996676

David W. Johnson & Roger T. Johnson. *Meaningful Assessment: A Manageable and Cooperative Process*, © 2002, Allyn & Bacon. 0205327621

Vernon F. Jones & Louise S. Jones. *Comprehensive Classroom Management: Creating Communities of Support and Solving Problems*, Sixth Edition, © 2001, Allyn & Bacon. 0205318509

Journal of Developmental Education, National Association for Developmental Education (NADE)

Michael B. Kane & Ruth Mitchell, eds. *Implementing Performance Assessment: Promises, Problems and Challenges*, © 1996, Lawrence Erlbaum Associates, Inc. 0805821325

Liping Ma. *Knowing and Teaching Elementary Mathematics*, © 1999, LEA Publishing.0805829091

Math Spanish Glossary, Second Edition, © 2001, Addison-Wesley. 0201728966

Mathematics Teacher, National Council of Teachers of Mathematics (NCTM) monthly journal.

John Meier, Thomas Rishel {MAA}, *Writing in the Teaching and Learning of Mathematics* © 1998, The Library of Congress, The Mathematical Association notes Number 48-86032.

Robert Müller, *The Great Book of Math Teasers*, © 1990, Sterling Publishing Co., Inc. 0806969539

W. James Popham. *Classroom Assessment: What Teachers Need to Know*, Third Edition, © 2002, Allyn & Bacon. 0205333044

Thomas A. Romberg, Editor. *Mathematics Assessment and Evaluation: Imperatives for Mathematics Educators*, © 1992, State University of New York Press. 0791409007

Ruth Stavy & Dina Tirosh. *How Students (Mis-) Understand Science and Mathematics*, © 2000, Teachers College Press, Columbia University. 0807739588

Linda Suskie. *Assessing Student Learning: A Common Sense Guide*, © 2004, Anker Publishing Company, Inc. 1882982711

David F. Treagust, Reinders Duit, & Barry J. Fraser, Editors. *Improving Teaching and Learning in Science and Mathematics*, © 1995, Teachers College Press, Columbia University. 0807734799

Carol Vorderman, *Reader's Digest How Math Works*, © 1996, Dorling Kindersley Limited, London. 0762102330

John Webb & Nitsa Movshovitz-Hadar. *One Equals Zero: And Other Mathematical Surprises,* © 1997, Key Curriculum Press. 1559533099

Norman L. Webb, Editor. *Assessment in the Mathematics Classroom,* © 1993, National Council of Teachers of Mathematics. 0873533526

Web Links

www.Algebra.com   Help with algebra homework on-line

www.AlgebraHelp.com   Math help using technology

www.amatyc.org   American Mathematics Association of Two Year Colleges

www.aw-bc.com/events   Addison-Wesley Workshop Site

www.mathxl.com   (see page 146 for more information)

www.coolmath.com   Resources for teachers and students. (some pages may require a subscription)

http://education.ti.com/educationportal/sites/US/sectionHome/download.html   Guidebooks for TI products and software downloads

http://hotmath.com   Homework help for different levels of math

www.ictcm.org   International Conference on Technology in Collegiate Mathematics

http://horizon.unc.edu/TS/   The Technology Source

www.joshhinds.com   A motivational and inspirational web site

www.maa.org   Mathematics Association of America

www.madeforsuccess.com   Chris Widener's site

www.mathnstuff.com   Descriptions for some good mathematics manipulatives.

http://mathforum.org/math.topics.html   The Math Forum at Drexel University

www.mathematicshelpcentral.com/graph_paper.htm   Site for printing out graph paper

www.mathbits.com   Fun math activities and lessons

http://www.mcli.dist.maricopa.edu/tl/   Teaching and Learning on the Web

www.merlot.org   Math applications, worksheets, puzzles, etc.

www.mymathlab.com   (see page 147 for more information)

www.nade.net   National Association for Developmental Education

www.nctm.org   The National Council of Teachers of Mathematics

www.purplemath.com   Algebra lessons

http://rubistar.4teachers.org   This free website helps teachers to make rubrics.

www.superkids.com   Including reviews of educational software

http://thesaurus.maths.org   Multi-lingual site containing explanations of math terms and ideas

http://turnbull.mcs.st-and.ac.uk/history   Historical information about math and mathematicians

www.uoregon.edu/~tep/technology/   University of Oregon Teaching Effectiveness Program

CONVERSION GUIDE

This conversion guide is designed to help you adapt your syllabus for Bittinger/ Ellenbogen/Johnson Intermediate Algebra: Graphs and Models, *Second Edition to Bittinger/Ellenbogen/Johnson* Intermediate Algebra: Graphs and Models, *Third Edition by providing a section-by-section cross reference between the two books. Additional revisions and refinements have been made in addition to the changes specified here.*

Chapter 9: Exponential and Logarithmic Functions	**Chapter 9: Exponential and Logarithmic Functions**
9.1 Composite and Inverse Functions	9.1 Composite and Inverse Functions
9.2 Exponential Functions	9.2 Exponential Functions
9.3 Logarithmic Functions	9.3 Logarithmic Functions
9.4 Properties of Logarithmic Functions	9.4 Properties of Logarithmic Functions
9.5 Natural Logarithms and Changing Bases	9.5 Natural Logarithms and Changing Bases
9.6 Solving Exponential and Logarithmic Equations	9.6 Solving Exponential and Logarithmic Equations
9.7 Applications of Exponential and Logarithmic Functions	9.7 Applications of Exponential and Logarithmic Functions
	Chapter 10: Conic Sections
Previously Appendix A	10.1 Conic Sections: Parabolas and Circles
Previously Appendix B	10.2 Conic Sections: Ellipses
Previously Appendix B	10.3 Conic Sections: Hyperbolas
Previously Appendix C	10.4 Nonlinear Systems of Equations
Chapter 10: Sequences, Series, and the Binomial Theorem	**Chapter 11: Sequences, Series, and the Binomial Theorem**
10.1 Sequences and Series	11.1 Sequences and Series
10.2 Arithmetic Sequences and Series	11.2 Arithmetic Sequences and Series
10.3 Geometric Sequences and Series	11.3 Geometric Sequences and Series
10.4 The Binomial Theorem	11.4 The Binomial Theorem
Appendices	**Appendices**
A Conic Sections: Parabolas and Circles (Now 10.1)	A Unit Conversion and Dimensional Analysis
B Conic Sections: Ellipses and Hyperbolas	Now 10.2 and 10.3
C Nonlinear Systems of Equations	Now 10.4

VIDEO AND EXERCISE INDEX

VHS Tape	DVT CD	Section	Chapter & Section Titles	Examples from Text Covered	Exercises from Text Covered
			Chapter 1 Basics of Algebra and Graphing		
1	1.1		Some Basics of Algebra	4, 9	15, 19, 37, 71
1	1.2		Operations with Real Numbers	3, 7c, 9b, 13	39, 47, 61, 63, 75, 79, 87, 93, 99, 113
1	1.3		Equivalent Algebraic Expressions	1, 2, 4, 5, 7, 10	11, 17, 31, 49, 57
1	1.4		Exponential and Scientific Notation	1b, 3, 5, 7b, 7c, 8b, 9b, 15	31, 51, 55, 111, 113, 123, 125
1	1.5		Graphs	1, 4, 7	21, 35, 47, 55
1	1.6		Solving Equations and Formulas	5, 6, 11, 12	11, 13, 17, 53, 59, 67, 77
1	1.7		Introduction to Problem Solving and Models	3, 5, 8	23, 69
			Chapter 2 Functions, Linear Equations, and Models		
2	2.1		Functions	5, 6	19
2	2.2		Linear Functions: Slope, Graphs, and Models	1, 5, 8	25, 59
2	2.3		Another Look at Linear Graphs	1, 2, 11	none
2	2.4		Introduction to Curve Fitting: Point-Slope Form	2, 5, 6	45, 61, 63
2	2.5		Domains and the Algebra of Functions	1, 2	45, 59, 64
			Chapter 3 Systems of Linear Equations and Problem Solving		
3	3.1		Systems of Equations in Two Variables	5a, 5b	13, 17
3	3.2		Solving by Substitution or Elimination	1, 3, 4, 7	11, 39
3	3.3		Solving Applications: Systems of Two Equations	none	38
3	3.4		Systems of Equations in Three Variables	1, 2, 4	35, 37
3	3.5		Solving Applications: Systems of Three Equations	3	3, 5
3	3.6		Elimination Using Matrices	3	7, 15
3	3.7		Determinants and Cramer's Rule	1, 2, 3, 4	9, 15, 17, 25
3	3.8		Business and Economics Applications	1	21
			Chapter 4 Inequalities and Problem Solving		
4	4.1		Inequalities and Applications	1, 3b, 7	21, 35, 37, 53
4	4.2		Solving Equations and Inequalities by Graphing	2, 3	25, 45, 49
4	4.3		Intersections, Unions, and Compound Inequalities	1, 2, 4, 5, 6	21, 33, 57
4	4.4		Absolute-Value Equations and Inequalities	1, 6, 7, 8	none
4	4.5		Inequalities in Two Variables	none	19, 55

VHS Tape	DVT CD	Section	Chapter & Section Titles	Examples from Text Covered	Exercises from Text Covered
			Chapter 5 Polynomials and Polynomials Functions		
4	5.1		Introduction to Polynomials and Polynomial Functions	3, 9	13, 96
4	5.2		Multiplication of Polynomials	1a, 2b, 3, 8a, 9a, 10a	31, 63
4	5.3		Polynomial Equations and Factoring	1, 2, 12	83, 107
4	5.4		Equations Containing Trinomials of the Type $x^2 + bx + c$	1, 11	15, 57, 67
5	5.5		Equations Containing Trinomials of the Type $ax^2 + bx + c$	1, 3, 5	21, 49, 67, 75
5	5.6		Equations Containing Perfect-Square Trinomials and Differences of Squares	2b, 3a, 8	36, 43
5	5.7		Equations Containing Sums or Differences of Cubes	1, 2a, 2d, 3	28, 42
5	5.8		Applications of Polynomial Equations	3	none
			Chapter 6 Rational Expressions, Equations, and Functions		
5	6.1		Rational Expressions and Functions: Multiplying and Dividing	1, 2, 6b, 9	41, 79
5	6.2		Rational Expressions and Functions: Adding and Subtracting	2, 4, 10	15, 39
5	6.3		Complex Rational Expressions	1, 3	14, 23, 43
5	6.4		Rational Equations	1, 3	23
5	6.5		Solving Applications Using Rational Equations	none	10, 21, 24
5	6.6		Division of Polynomials	5	44, 17, 21
6	6.7		Synthetic Division	1	15, 25
6	6.8		Formulas, Applications, and Variation	6	16, 41, 66, 71, 73
			Chapter 7 Exponents and Radical Functions		
6	7.1		Radical Expressions, Functions, and Models	3, 5, 8, 14	9, 21, 23, 53, 61, 65, 95, 103
6	7.2		Rational Numbers as Exponents	1a, 2b, 4a, 7c, 8d, 9c	19, 29, 33, 45, 62, 102
6	7.3		Multiplying Radical Expressions	4a	8, 16, 28, 45, 49, 58
6	7.4		Dividing Radical Expressions	1a, 2a, 4a, 5a, 5c	33, 39, 69
6	7.5		Expressions Containing Several Radical Terms	1a, 1c, 3c	32, 85, 96
6	7.6		Solving Radical Equations	1, 5	40
6	7.7		Geometric Applications	3, 6	19, 23, 35, 37
6	7.8		The Complex Numbers	2, 4	9, 15, 19, 37, 47, 53, 69, 73, 87, 89, 93
			Chapter 8 Quadratic Functions and Equations		
7	8.1		Quadratic Equations	2	71
7	8.2		The Quadratic Formula	none	9, 13, 37
7	8.3		Applications Involving Quadratic Equations	4	3, 15
7	8.4		Studying Solutions of Quadratic Equations	1b, 2b	11, 14, 50
7	8.5		Equations Reducible to Quadratic	2, 3	12, 23
7	8.6		Quadratic Functions and Their Graphs	1	27, 53
7	8.7		More About Graphing Quadratic Functions	1, 3	39, 47
7	8.8		Problem Solving and Quadratic Functions	none	13
7	8.9		Polynomial and Rational Inequalities	1, 5	39

VHS Tape	DVT CD	Section	Chapter & Section Titles	Examples from Text Covered	Exercises from Text Covered
			Chapter 9 Exponential and Logarithmic Functions		
8	9.1		Composite and Inverse Functions	none	41, 43
8	9.2		Exponential Functions	1, 2	33
8	9.3		Logarithmic Functions	3	9, 17, 19, 47, 51, 73, 85, 97, 99, 103
8	9.4		Properties of Logarithmic Functions	2, 3, 9a	7, 25, 41, 51
8	9.5		Natural Logarithms and Changing Bases	1, 3	35, 83
8	9.6		Solving Exponential and Logarithmic Equations	1, 6	45
8	9.7		Applications of Exponential and Logarithmic Functions	1, 5	3, 35
			Chapter 10 Conic Sections		
9	10.1		Conic Sections: Parabolas and Circles	1, 4	25, 45, 59, 77, 87
9	10.2		Conic Sections: Ellipses	1	13, 29, 31
9	10.3		Conic Sections: Hyperbolas	2	11, 21
9	10.4		Nonlinear Systems of Equations	3, 4	8, 38, 47
			Chapter 11 Sequences, Series, and the Binomial Theorem		
9	11.1		Sequences and Series	3b, 5a	14, 30, 47, 55, 65
9	11.2		Arithmetic Sequences and Series	1b, 5	none
9	11.3		Geometric Sequences and Series	none	13, 61, 67
9	11.4		The Binomial Theorem	4a, 6	47

ADDITIONAL
COLLABORATIVE CORNERS

Chapter 1: No Room for Emergencies

Collaborative Corner

No Room for Emergencies

Focus: Models

Time: 20 minutes

Group size: 3

The number of emergency room visits throughout the United States is increasing, due in part to a greater number of people seeking emergency treatment for illnesses that require routine medical care. At the same time, the number of hospitals is decreasing. Use the information in the following table to perform the listed activities. (*Sources*: U.S. Bureau of the Census; *Statistical Abstract of the United States*, 2000; *The New York Times Almanac*, 2002; Centers for Disease Control; www.cdc.gov)

Year	Number of Emergency Room Visits	Number of Hospitals	Number of Emergency Room Visits per Hospital	U.S. Population	Number of Emergency Room Visits per Person
1995	95,000,000	6291		263,082,000	
1996	94,000,000	6201		265,502,000	
1997	95,000,000	6097		268,048,000	
1998	100,000,000	6021		270,509,000	
1999	103,000,000	5890		272,945,000	
2000	108,000,000	5800		281,422,000	

ACTIVITY

1. Calculate, as a group, the number of emergency room visits per hospital and the number of emergency room visits per person for the years 1995 to 2000. Record that information in the table in the appropriate columns.

2. Each group member should choose one of the following columns:

   Number of emergency room visits;

   Number of emergency room visits per hospital;

   Number of emergency room visits per person.

He or she should create a line graph, using the figures in that column on the vertical axis and the corresponding years on the horizontal axis.

3. On the basis of the line graph created, each group member should determine whether the following statement appears to be true:

   "The number of emergency room visits in the United States is increasing."

4. Compare the graphs.

5. Working together as a group, write a sentence or paragraph that describes what each graph indicates.

Chapter 1: Who Pays What?

Who Pays What?

Focus: Problem solving

Time: 15 minutes

Group size: 5

Suppose that two of the five members in each group are celebrating birthdays and the entire group goes out to lunch. Suppose further that each member whose birthday it is gets treated to his or her lunch by the other *four* members. Finally, suppose that all meals cost the same amount and that the total bill is $40.00.*

*This activity was inspired by "The Birthday-Lunch Problem," *Mathematics Teaching in the Middle School,* vol. 2, no. 1, September–October 1996, pp. 40–42.

ACTIVITY

1. Determine, as a group, how much each group member should pay for the lunch described above. Then explain how this determination was made.

2. Compare the results and methods used for part (1) with those of the other groups in the class.

Chapter 2: Calculating License Fees

Collaborative Corner

Calculating License Fees

Focus: Functions
Time: 15–20 minutes
Group size: 3–4

The California Department of Motor Vehicles calculates automobile registration fees (VLF) according to the schedule shown below.

ACTIVITY

1. Determine the original sale price of the oldest vehicle owned by a member of your group. If necessary, use the price and age of a family member's vehicle. Be sure to note the year in which the car was purchased.

2. Use the schedule below to calculate the vehicle license fee (VLF) for the vehicle in part (1) above for each year from the year of purchase to the present. To speed your work, each group member can find the fee for a few different years.

3. Graph the results from part (2). On the *x*-axis, plot years beginning with the year of purchase, and on the *y*-axis, plot $V(x)$, the VLF as a function of year.

4. What is the lowest VLF that the owner of this car will ever have to pay, according to this schedule? Compare your group's answer with other groups' answers.

5. Does your group feel that California's method for calculating registration fees is fair? Why or why not? How could it be improved?

6. Try, as a group, to find an algebraic form for the function $y = V(x)$.

7. *Optional out-of-class extension*: Create a program for a graphing calculator that accepts two inputs (initial value of the vehicle and year of purchase) and produces $V(x)$ as the output.

DMV VEHICLE LICENSE FEE INFORMATION

A Public Service Agency

The 2% **Vehicle License Fee (VLF)** is in lieu of a personal property tax on vehicles. Most VLF revenue is returned to City and County Local Governments (see reverse side). The license fee charged is based upon the sale price or vehicle value when initially registered in California. The vehicle value is adjusted for any subsequent sale or transfer, that occurred 8/19/91 or later, excluding sales or transfers between specified relatives.

The VLF is calculated by rounding the sale price to the nearest **odd** hundred dollar. That amount is reduced by a percentage utilizing an eleven year schedule (shown to the right), and 2% of that amount is the fee charged. See the accompanying example for a vehicle purchased last year for $9,199. This would be the second registration year following that purchase.

WHERE DO YOUR DMV FEES GO? SEE REVERSE SIDE.

DMV77 8(REV.6/95)   95 30123

PERCENTAGE SCHEDULE
Rev. & Tax. Code Sec. 10753.2
(Trailer coaches have a different schedule)

1st Year	100%	7th Year	40%
2nd Year	90%	8th Year	30%
3rd Year	80%	9th Year	25%
4th Year	70%	10th year	20%
5th Year	60%	11th Year	
6th Year	50%	onward	15%

VLF CALCULATION EXAMPLE

Purchase Price:	$9,199
Rounded to:	$9,100
Times the Percentage:	90%
Equals Fee Basis of:	$8,190
Times 2% Equals:	$163.80
Rounded to:	$164

Chapter 4: Save on Shipping Costs

Saving on Shipping Costs

Focus: Compound inequalities and
          solution sets

Time: 20 – 30 minutes

Group size: 2 – 3

At present (2002), the U.S. Postal Service charges 23 cents per ounce plus an additional 14-cent delivery fee (1 oz or less costs 37 cents; more than 1 oz, but not more than 2 oz, costs 60 cents; and so on). Rapid Delivery charges $1.05 per pound plus an additional $2.50 delivery fee (up to 16 oz costs $3.55; more than 16 oz, but less than or equal to 32 oz, costs $4.60; and so on). Let *x* be the weight, in ounces, of an item being mailed.*

_____

*Based on an article by Michael Contino in *Mathematics Teacher,* May 1995.

ACTIVITY

One group member should determine the function *p*, where *p*(*x*) represents the cost, in dollars, of mailing *x* ounces at a post office. Another group member should determine the function *r*, where *r*(*x*) represents the cost, in dollars, of mailing *x* ounces with Rapid Delivery. The third group member should graph *p* and *r* on the same set of axes. Finally, working together, use the graph to determine those weights for which the Postal Service is less expensive. Express your answer using both set-builder and interval notation.

Chapter 4: The Rule of 85

Collaborative Corner

The Rule of 85

Focus: Linear inequalities
Time: 20–30 minutes
Group size: 3

Under a proposed "Rule of 85," full-time faculty in the California State Teachers Retirement System (kindergarten through community college) who are a years old with y years of service would have the option of retirement if $a + y \geq 85$.

ACTIVITY

1. Decide, as a group, the age range of full-time teachers. Express this age range as an inequality involving a.

2. Decide, as a group, the number of years someone could teach full-time before retiring. Express this answer as a compound inequality involving y.

3. Using the Rule of 85 and the answers to parts (1) and (2) above, write a system of inequalities. Then, using a scale of 5 yr per square, graph the system. To facilitate comparisons with graphs from other groups, plot a on the horizontal axis and y on the vertical axis.

4. Compare the graphs from all groups. Try to reach consensus on the graph that most clearly illustrates what the status would be of someone who would have the option of retirement under the Rule of 85.

5. If your instructor is agreeable to the idea, attempt to represent him or her with a point on your graph.

Chapter 6: Does the Model Hold Water?

Does the Model Hold Water?

Focus: Testing a mathematical model

Time: 20–30 minutes

Group size: 2–3

Materials: An empty 1-gal plastic jug, a kitchen or laboratory sink, a stopwatch or a watch capable of measuring seconds, an inexpensive pen or pair of scissors or a nail or knife for poking holes in plastic.

Problems like Exercises 49 and 50 can be solved algebraically and then checked at home or in a laboratory.

ACTIVITY

1. While one group member fills the empty jug with water, the other group member(s) should record how many seconds this takes.

2. After carefully poking a few holes in the bottom of the jug, record how many seconds it takes the full jug to empty.

3. Using the information found in parts (1) and (2) above, use algebra to predict how long it will take to fill the punctured jug.

4. Test your prediction by timing how long it takes for the pierced jug to be filled. Be sure to run the water at the same rate as in part (1).

5. How accurate was your prediction? How might your prediction have been made more accurate?

Chapter 6: How Many Is a Million?

Collaborative Corner

How Many Is a Million?

Focus: Direct variation and estimation

Time: 15 minutes

Group size: 2 or 3 and entire class

The National Park Service's estimates of crowd sizes for static (stationary) mass demonstrations vary directly as the area covered by the crowd. Park Service officials have found that at basic "shoulder-to-shoulder" demonstrations, 1 acre of land (about 45,000 ft^2) holds about 9000 people. Using aerial photographs, officials impose a grid to estimate the total area covered by the demonstrators. Once this has been accomplished, estimates of crowd size can be prepared.

ACTIVITY

1. In the grid imposed on the photograph below, each square represents 10,000 ft^2. Estimate the size of the crowd photographed. Then compare your group's estimate with those of other groups. What might explain discrepancies between estimates? List ways in which your group's estimate could be made more accurate.

2. Park Service officials use an "acceptable margin of error" of no more than 20%. Using all estimates from part (1) above and allowing for error, find a range of values within which you feel certain that the actual crowd size lies.

3. The Million Man March of 1995 was not a static demonstration because of a periodic turnover of people in attendance (many people stayed for only part of the day's festivities). How might you change your methodology to compensate for this complication?

Chapter 8: Quadratic Counter Settings

Quadratic Counter Settings

Focus: Modeling quadratic functions

Time: 20–30 minutes

Group size: 3 or 4

Materials: Graphing calculators are optional.

The Panasonic Portable Stereo System RX-DT680® has a counter for finding locations on an audio cassette. When a fully wound cassette with 45 min of music on a side begins to play, the counter is at 0. After 15 min of music has played, the counter reads 250, and after 35 min, it reads 487. When the 45-min side is finished playing, the counter reads 590.

ACTIVITY

1. The paragraph above describes four ordered pairs of the form (counter number, minutes played). Three pairs are enough to find a function of the form

$$T(n) = an^2 + bn + c,$$

where $T(n)$ is the time, in minutes, that the tape has run at counter reading n hundred. Each group member should select a different set of three points from the four given and then fit a quadratic function to the data.

2. Of the 3 or 4 functions found in part (1) above, which fits the data "best"? One way to answer this is to see how well each function predicts other pairs. The same counter used above reads 432 after a 45-min tape has played for 30 min. Which function comes closest to predicting this?

3. *Optional*: Use regression to fit a quadratic function to the data. How well does this function predict the reading after 30 min?

4. If a class member has access to a Panasonic System RX-DT680, see how well the functions developed above predict the counter readings for a tape that has played for 5 or 10 min.

Chapter 9: Television Rights

Collaborative Corner

Television Rights

Focus: Models
Time: 20 minutes
Group size: 3 – 6

Sometimes simply looking at the graph of a particular set of data will give a good indication of an appropriate model for the data. Often, more than one type of model is a possibility. One way to determine which is the best model is to calculate several possible functions, graph them along with the data, and determine which one seems to best fit the data. Another indication of a good model is its ability to predict another, known, data point not included in determining the model.

ACTIVITY

The following table shows the amount that television networks have either paid or agreed to pay for the television rights to the Summer Olympic Games.

Year	Amount Paid for Television Rights (in millions)
1968	$ 4.5
1972	7.5
1976	25
1980	87
1984	225
1988	300
1992	401
1996	456
2000	705
2004	793

Source: NBC Sports

1. Each group member should graph the data. The group should then agree on at least two possible models for the data from the following list: linear, quadratic, cubic, quartic, or exponential. (See the library of functions on the inside front cover.)

2. Form a model of each type chosen in part (1), and graph each model along with the data. Determine, as a group, which model appears to fit the data best.

3. NBC has agreed to pay $894 million for the television rights to the 2008 Summer Olympics. Determine, as a group, which model best predicts this amount.